DATE DUE

AN ILLUSTRATED GUIDE TO SOME POISONOUS PLANTS AND ANIMALS OF FLORIDA

AN ILLUSTRATED GUIDE TO SOME POISONOUS PLANTS AND ANIMALS OF FLORIDA

George R. Campbell

Illustrated by

Ann L. Winterbotham

Pineapple Press, Inc.
Englewood, Florida

The author and illustrator dedicate this book to
George C. Tenney

Library of Congress Cataloging in Publication Data
Campbell, George R. (George Robert), 1918–
An illustrated guide to some poisonous plants and animals of Florida.

Bibliography: p.
Includes index.
1. Poisonous animals—Florida—Identification.
2. Poisonous plants—Florida—Identification. 3. First aid in illness and injury. I. Winterbotham, Ann L.
II. Title.
QL100.C28 1983 574.6'5 83-61760
ISBN 0-910923-04-3

Published by Pineapple Press, Inc.
P.O. Box 314
Englewood, Florida 33533

Printed in the United States of America.

FIRST AID
AFTER SUSPECTED POISONING

The most important first aid is to call the Emergency Medical Service in your area. They will send the nearest emergency unit. It should be only a matter of minutes before an ambulance with trained paramedics will reach you.

Some items in this book are of minor importance (mild Poison Ivy dermatitis, some insect bites or stings). In such cases, elementary first aid as described under each species will usually suffice. However, if the victim is allergic to bee stings, for example, the situation should be considered an emergency.

In the case of medical problems involving organisms distinguished in the text by a skull and crossbones symbol, Emergency Medical Service should ALWAYS be called.

THINGS TO DO

Emesis will remove most plant poisons most efficiently, so induce VOMITING in most cases of ingestion of plant material: leaves, fruits, berries, seeds. Place finger or blunt instrument in the throat to induce vomiting. Ipecac Syrup (half teaspoonful for children, one or two tablespoonfuls for adults) is better, if available. Follow with slightly warm water. However, if you have called Emergency Services, the paramedics will have arrived and will handle induced emesis or possibly gastric lavage, if indicated. Save samples of vomitus. Also save specimens of offending plant parts, if possible.

THINGS NOT TO DO

Do not induce vomiting if the patient is in a coma or is having (or has had) convulsions.

ACKNOWLEDGMENTS

Many people have helped in many ways in the preparation of this book. Among them are . . .

David Campbell
Jean Campbell
Dr. George Cooley
Kathy Doggett, Paramedic
Phyllis J. Douglass, D.V.M.
K. C. Emerson, Ph.D.
Jean W. Gentry, M.D.
Stephan S. Halabis, M.D.
Prof. Dr. E. Hecker
Barbara Valentine Hertz
David B. Hertz, Ph.D.
Deborah Hill
Keith Knight, R.N.
Karen Lowell, M.S.
Denis Radefeld, M.D.
Tom Sharp
James K. Stoller, M.D.
George C. Tenney
Diane Walters
William L. Webb, Ph.D.

PREFACE

This book has been in preparation for more than two years. Each day of study reveals new toxic or venomous organisms that can be found in Florida or new and sometimes frightening details of some plants or animals already included. Another year (or six) could be spent adding species and detail, but everything has to end. What follows is the best effort to date (mid-1983).

Properly used by victims, their families and friends and by emergency medical personnel and physicians, the information in this book can, perhaps, save lives and may prevent a lot of pain and suffering. The work is also designed to inform on a broad and interesting biological subject as well as to be of practical value. So do enjoy it!

George R. Campbell

HOW TO USE THIS BOOK

It would be impossible to catalogue each and every poisonous or venomous plant and animal of Florida.

However every effort has been made, through description and illustration, to enable one to identify an organism, or its near relative, that may be causing a problem.

Most of the descriptions are written in lay terms. Unavoidable technical biological or medical language is sometimes used for brevity and precision. A good dictionary will suffice to clarify any ambiguities. A limited glossary may be found in the back of the book.

A Skull and Crossbones symbol identifies some organisms. All species in the book are either venomous or poisonous. The Skull and Crossbones symbol indicates those which, in our opinion, are *most dangerous*.

IN AN EMERGENCY, CALL THE EMERGENCY MEDICAL SERVICE IN YOUR AREA.

1. Recognize symptoms. Take notes for use when discussing the case with emergency personnel or, later, the doctor.
2. Try to identify the offending organism.
3. Collect specimens of the offending organism. A photograph could prove to be useful if the organism is so big or revolting that it can't be easily collected.
4. Administer first aid as indicated.

Suggested emergency first aid equipment:

Fels-Naptha Bar Soap
Adolph's Meat Tenderizer
Antihistamines if there is an allergic person in the house
Peroxide
Calamine
Aloe

CONTENTS

PREFACE vii

INTRODUCTION xi

POISONOUS SUBSTANCES PRODUCED BY PLANTS . . . 3

CO-CARCINOGENIC PLANT PRODUCTS 5

SECTION I: POISONOUS PLANTS 9

SECTION II: TOXIC AND VENOMOUS ANIMALS 101

INVERTEBRATE ANIMALS 105

VERTEBRATE ANIMALS 145

A LIMITED GLOSSARY 161

BIBLIOGRAPHY 165

INDEX 167

INDEX TO SYMPTOMS

PLANTS 173

ANIMALS 174

INTRODUCTION

The ever-increasing number of visitors to, and residents of, the State of Florida in recent years has indicated that there is a real need for a catalogue of hazardous organisms, both plant and animal, to be found here. There are also those readers whose interest in poisonous plants and venomous animals is that of the naturalist or student of biological phenomena.

As one who has studied this subject for many years, I was pleased to have been asked to write this volume, and to have the help and expertise of Ann L. Winterbotham who not only illustrated it, but also brought to the effort a great deal of botanical knowledge.

Everybody has heard about Coral Snakes, Rattlesnakes, and Widow Spiders, so perhaps the most significant contribution that can be made by this work is in the area of poisonous plants that occur here either naturally or as cultivated exotics. However, there is also much interest in the animals, both terrestrial and marine, and as a consequence we have tried to cover the significantly important creatures, great and small, as well as many of the known toxic plants. No doubt we have inadvertently omitted some forms. If you find significant omissions, please write and, if warranted, they will be added to future printings.

While the main thrust relates to organisms that might be harmful to the human animal, we have not ignored the veterinary aspects of this subject and, when appropriate, have mentioned plants and animals that can be harmful to domestic animals.

Also, when an organism has a medical application, we have made an effort to cite it whether it be used in modern medicine, as is the Periwinkle, or in local folk medicine, as were the Stoppers of genus *Eugenia*.

Many of our most beautiful exotic cultivars and weed invaders contain poisonous or toxic principles that are very dangerous to humans or other animals. Among the wild indigenous plants there are quite a few that contain poisonous compounds that can be very damaging.

Some plants are sometimes toxic and at other times edible, depending on the stage of development. We have made every effort to cite these.

In some cases a plant may have a toxic part next to an edible part; e.g., *Momordica.*

In regard to fungi (mushrooms), we advise that all species should be avoided. We suggest they be left to the Box Turtles and Gopher Tortoises which seem to be immune to mushroom toxins. Thus the discussion of mushrooms will be found to be generalized.

This book is directed to all who share interest in our plants and animals and to those children and adults who may suffer from too close contact with those that are toxic or venomous. The book is not in any way intended to substitute for professional medical attention. Many of the plants described in this book are dangerously poisonous and their ingestion can be fatal. Some of the venomous animals described can be lethal. The author advises against any type of self or non-professional treatment based on the information given, and neither he nor the publisher takes any responsibility for the outcome of any such experimentation.

If there is *any* health problem at all involving any of the organisms discussed in this book, or any other Florida organisms inadvertently omitted from this book, the author *urges* you to call your local Emergency Medical Service.

AN ILLUSTRATED GUIDE TO SOME POISONOUS PLANTS AND ANIMALS OF FLORIDA

POISONOUS SUBSTANCES PRODUCED BY PLANTS

It is beyond the scope of this work to do much more than name the various classifications of poisonous principles that are found in the plant world. Those seeking more information on any of the following named groups may consult the pharmacological and chemical literature.

The significant poisonous principles found in plants are:

Alkaloids—not true bases, but with "alkali-like" properties. Alkaloids are by far the most numerous of the toxins found in plants and many are produced by plants discussed in this work; e.g., those of *Datura, Ervatamia,* and *Solanum.*

Polypeptides and Amines. Mushrooms such as *Amanita* contain toxic peptides.

Phytotoxins (also known as Toxalbumins). Among the phytotoxins there are several which occur here that are extremely toxic. For example, ricin in the Castor Bean, and abrin in the Precatory Pea.

Glycosides (sometimes spelled Glucosides). In this group there are many: some that generate cyanide, some that are goiterogenic, those with irritant oils, cumerin glycosides that interfere with blood coagulation which can be considered to be hemorrhagic agents, cardiac glycosides and saponins.

Oxylates.

Resins and allied materials.

Compounds causing photosensitivity.

Not all plant poisons can be categorized in the above list. Many plants contain principles that are either not easily classified or ones of which the molecular structure is as yet unknown.

Also omitted from the above list are minerals: selenium, nitrogen, copper, lead, cadmium, fluorine, and molybdenum compounds.

In addition to toxic chemical principles that are produced by plants and can cause health problems to people and animals, one must not overlook the purely mechanical aspects of injury from some plants. Florida is abundantly supplied with cacti and agaves, not to mention super-sharp-pointed yuccas, all of which can inflict serious wounds to children and sometimes animals. These plants can be rendered safer, without appreciably sacrificing garden beauty, by amputating their terminal thorns. Wounds from these plants can take a long time to heal. In such cases, I suspect that a toxic element may have been introduced with the thorn puncture; e.g., *Yucca.*

CO-CARCINOGENIC PLANT PRODUCTS

There is one group of plants so commonly grown in Florida that special consideration of their cancer-producing properties will be discussed briefly here. Reference is made to that large group, the Spurge Family, Euphorbiaceae.

Through good fortune we have been able to correspond with Prof. Dr. E. Hecker of Heidelberg, Dr. James K. Stoller of Boston, and Dr. Denis Radefeld of Ohio. All of these scientists generously shared their knowledge with us.

Members of the Euphorbiaceae are popular in Florida. Many species are grown extensively here, mostly for ornamental landscape purposes. One, the Poinsettia, is very widely used at Christmas and is perhaps the most common ornamental of that season. Present knowledge would indicate it to be without co-carcinogenic qualities, but the writer retains an open-minded suspicion.

Many members of this family contain some of the most potent co-carcinogens known to science. In the simplest terms, co-carcinogens activate submanifestational (or subcarcinogenic) doses of solitary carcinogens, which together produce or promote cancer.

There are three groups of Euphorbic species that contain three different, but chemically related, diterpene hydrocarbons which give rise to potent cancer-promoting agents. The following listed plants are divided and organized to reflect their relationship to the three diterpene hydrocarbons, tigliane, daphnane, ingenane.

Those producing tigliane:
- Pencil Tree, *Euphorbia tirucalli*
- Bellyache Bush, *Jatropha gossypifolia*
- Coral Plant, *Jatropha multifida*
- Physic Nut, *Jatropha curas*

That producing daphnane:
- Sand Box Tree, *Hura crepitans*
  (A West Indian tree sometimes grown in Florida. This species also produces both tigliane and ingenane.)

Those producing ingenane:
Candelabra "Cactus," *Euphorbia lactea*
Crown of Thorns, *Euphorbia milii (splendens)*
Pencil Tree, *Euphorbia tirucalli*

There are many other Euphorbs cultivated and native here.

In using this book, it will be well to consider *all* members of the Euphorbiaceae as being potentially hazardous. The family of each described plant is shown, so it will not be difficult to adjust your thinking whenever the word Euphorbiaceae appears.

The World Health Organization has estimated that 85% of all human cancer is related to environmental factors, not industrial technology. Such risk factors seem to be extremely abundant throughout South Florida. Probably the growing of one or several of these Euphorbic plants in the garden is harmless enough if care is exercised in their placement and cultivation.

The white sap of many Euphorbic species should be a danger signal. Avoid it. Use care in pruning and elimination of the resultant leaves and stems. Avoid carrying armfuls. Avoid burning them. Wear protective goggles when working with Euphorbs.

The horticulturalist or landscaper who propagates these species, or the worker who constantly and repeatedly comes in contact with the Pencil Tree, which grows vigorously in South Florida, should realize that he is placing himself *at risk* unless care is taken to avoid exposure.

Professor Dr. E. Hecker who, with his co-workers, has been handling Euphorbs and the substances they produce for more than fifteen years has this advice to offer:

Exposure by Contact

"In any event, the bulk of the latex on the skin or mucous membranes should be washed off as quickly as possible using plenty of running water. If possible (except in the case of mucous membranes) washing by soap should follow. If the skin exposed has already begun to itch, because for example exposure was not noticed, after treatment as above, the area exposed may be creamed with some cortisone ointment or cortisone lotion; the latter especially in the case of mucous membranes. Eye exposure is very painful, as I experienced personally while pruning Euphorbs in my garden since I forgot to wear *protective eye glasses—please recommend!*—and after washing with plenty of running water consultation of an ophthalmologist is necessary for administration of a cortisone-containing eye lotion."

Exposure by Ingestion

"This type of exposure should be avoided definitely. It probably does not happen in adults, but inexperienced children, dogs, or other pets, may pick leaves, for example, and put them into their mouths."

For information relative to another plant of interest in relation to cancer, see *Zamia floridana,* the cycad called Coontie which may be the only Florida plant that contains solitary carcinogenic substance.

SECTION I
POISONOUS PLANTS

"What a curious feeling!" said Alice.
"I must be shutting up like a telescope."

ARRANGEMENT OF THE PLANTS

The plants are arranged alphabetically by family. Most shown are angiosperms. No effort is made to arrange the angiosperm families other than alphabetically. That is, dicotyledon families and monocotyledon families are interspersed because it was felt that emphasis on phylogenetic relationships in a work of this kind would add no value. Exceptions are (1) the generalized commentary on mushrooms and (2) the Coontie which appear first in the book. Mushrooms are, of course, fungi, and the Coontie is a gymnosperm related to the pines, thus they are more primitive than any of the angiosperms. The discussion of "Farmer's Lung" under the "Australian Pine" could logically be placed near the mushroom because the causative agent(s) is (are) probably due to molds or other fungi.

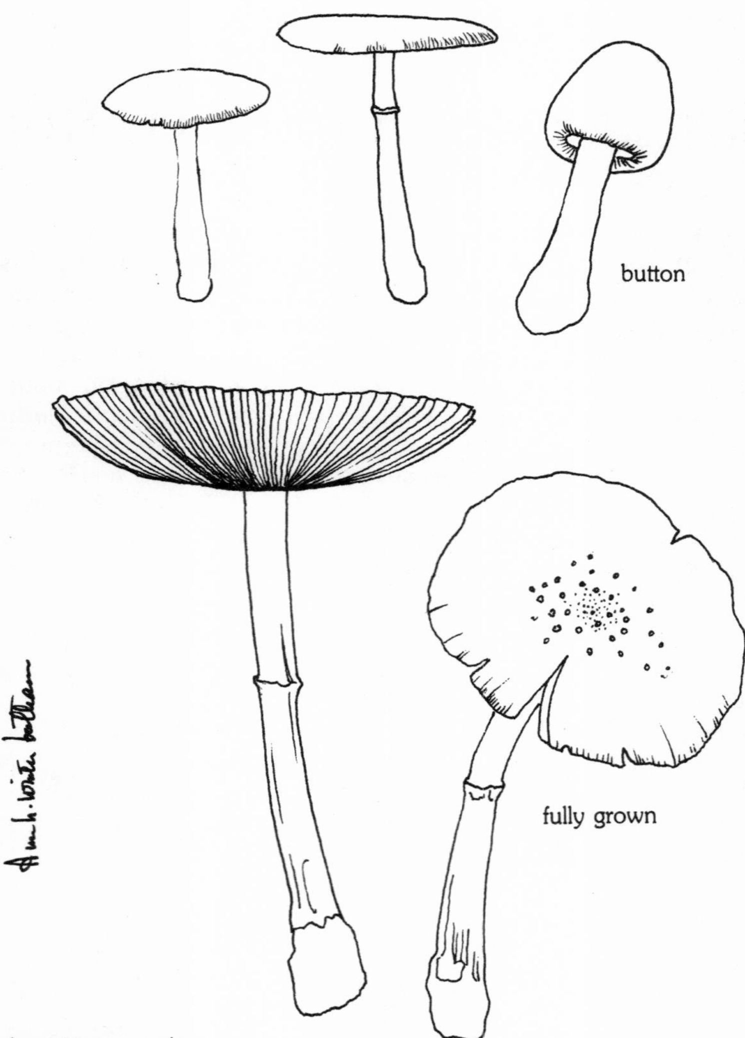

Amanita muscaria
Fly Mushroom is believed to be the "Magic Mushroom" of Lewis Carroll

MOST COMMON NAME: FLY AGARIC

WHERE FOUND

Damp gardens, lawns, wood chips, compost, wild places, often grows in "Fairy Rings."

COMMON NAMES	SCIENTIFIC NAME
FLY AGARIC	*Amanita muscaria*
Fly Mushroom	
Magic Mushroom	AMANITACEAE
(of Alice in Wonderland)	The AMANITA FAMILY

DESCRIPTION

Dirty gray to whitish or yellowish mushroom cap, 2″ to 6″ in diameter, sometimes with light cotton-like patches. All *Amanita* species grow from an egg-like "Universal Veil," the shell of which fragments and sticks to the growing "button," resulting in the light cotton-like patches that may be seen on the cap. Stalk has ring and swollen basal bulb. Gills many and off-white. White spore print.

NATURE OF TOXICITY

Amanita muscaria is considered to be poisonous although not usually deadly. It does contain toxic compounds that cause drowsiness, deep sleep and disorientation. It contains muscarine which is related to choline as well as hallucinogenic compounds that act on the nervous system. There are many other *Amanita* species such as the Destroying Angel, *A. virosa,* and the Deathcap Mushroom, *A. phalloides.* Both of these are very widespread in their ranges and are DEADLY in their toxicity. They and many other mushrooms contain complex polypeptides; in these cases, amanitine and phalloidine. See Poisonous Substances Produced by Plants, page 3.

SYMPTOMS

In the case of *Amanita muscaria* ingestion, symptoms are watering of the eyes and mouth, sweating, slow heartbeat, contraction of the pupils, difficulty in breathing, abdominal cramps, vomiting, hallucination, collapse, possible convulsions and coma.

FIRST AID

Seek emergency medical aid when any mushroom poisoning is suspected. Preserve specimens of vomitus and, if possible, of the mushroom involved, thus providing an opportunity for positive identification.

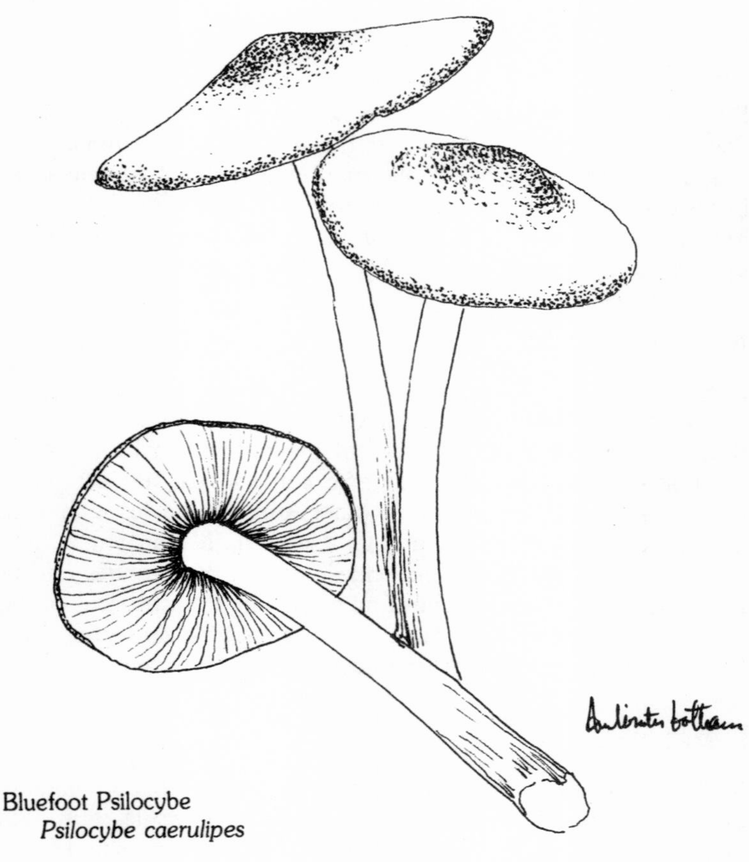

Bluefoot Psilocybe
Psilocybe caerulipes

This species and its relatives are unwisely consumed for their hallucinogenic properties.

REMARKS

Safe mushrooms are available in nearly every supermarket. It is therefore hard to understand why there are so many *mycophagists,* as people who eat mushrooms might be called, who repair to the woods and, with suicidal fervor, gather mushrooms with sometimes fatal results.

It is not the purpose of this book to dwell at length on mushrooms. *Amanita muscaria* was the species chosen to discuss because of its wide geographical range and special interest and fame, it being the Magic Mushroom of Alice in Wonderland. There are many species in the principle genus of this family, *Amanita,* and it is these mushrooms that cause by far the most fatalities.

The above remarks are all that appear in this work on the subject of Mushrooms. OUR ADVICE IS EMPHATIC: DO NOT CONSUME WILD MUSHROOMS. Each year some 500 mycetismus (mushroom poisoning) cases are reported in the USA, some fatal. There are recent records of expert mycologists succumbing to mycetismus.

Zamia floridana

MOST COMMON NAME: COONTIE

WHERE FOUND

Rare in the wild, but cultivated by some. Allied forms (i.e., other cycads) are widely planted in gardens.

COMMON NAMES	SCIENTIFIC NAMES
COONTIE Florida Arrowroot	*Zamia floridana* (Syns.) *Z. pumila* *Z. integrifolia*
	CYCADACEAE The CYCAD FAMILY

DESCRIPTION

Gymnosperm (looks like palm or fern, but relative of pines). Compound leaves, arranged in rosette. Stem usually completely underground, swollen; sweet potato-shaped. *Washed and cooked,* it provided Indians with useful starch for Seminole bread, *Conti hateka.* Sexes separate, male cones 4+″ long, female cone 3½″-4″ long, 3″ diameter; seeds orange yellow ½″. Long-lived of ancient lineage. Cycads contributed substantially to fossil fuel—principally coal.

NATURE OF TOXICITY

The underground root must be grated and washed many times to remove the poison, Cycasin. Wash water is reddish.

The toxic principles identified by Dr. M. Whiting in her worldwide study of cycad toxicity are cycasin, methyllazoxy methanol and N-methyldiamin-opropionic acid. There is evidence of *carcinogenicity* in rats which have been fed seed husks of cycads.

SYMPTOMS

Vomiting, abdominal cramps, severe gastric upset, bloody diarrhea, bloody lung congestion, ataxia (wobbles, limber-leg, peculiar locomotion, unbalanced stance), paralysis. There are examples of seeds poisoning human beings. They are said to be somewhat narcotic. Pollen from male cones of some cycads causes respiratory distress in Florida. Japanese workers have identified toxic azoxyglycosides in some cycad forms.

FIRST AID

Induce vomiting. Seek medical aid.

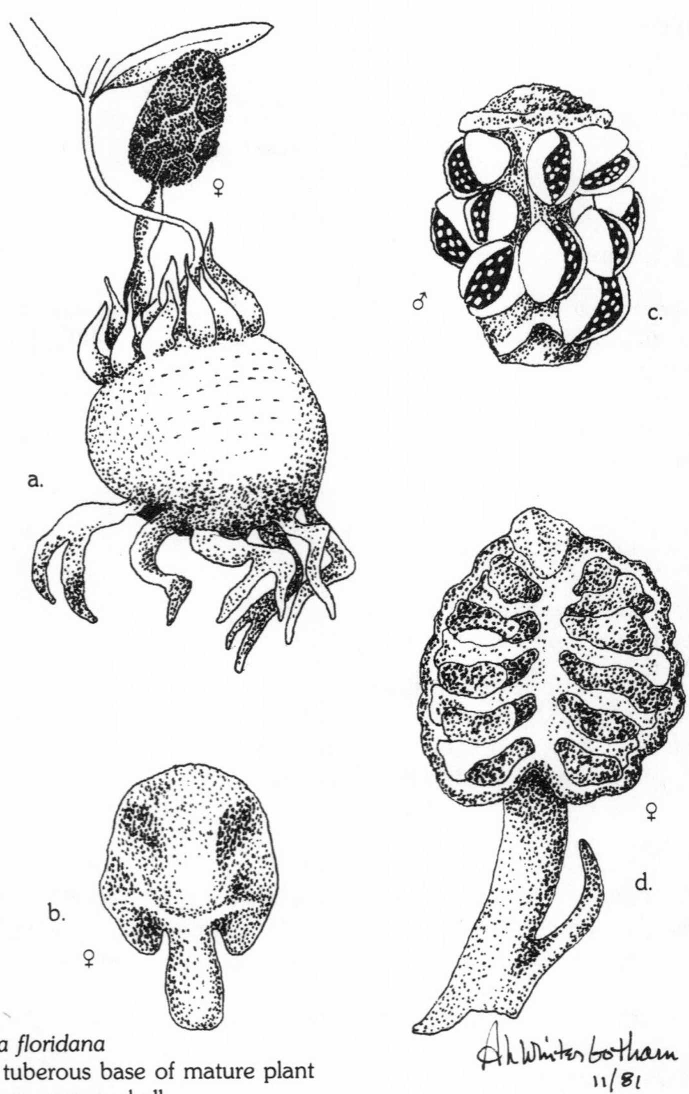

Zamia floridana
a. tuberous base of mature plant
b. megasporophyll
c. microsporophyll
d. mature ovulate strobilus

REMARKS

Other cycads of the genera *Cycas* and *Macrozamia* grown as specimen plants here are known to be toxic although some are also used as a starch source in other lands. We suggest that it is all right to grow cycads but don't try to prepare any food from them, and keep seeds away from children.

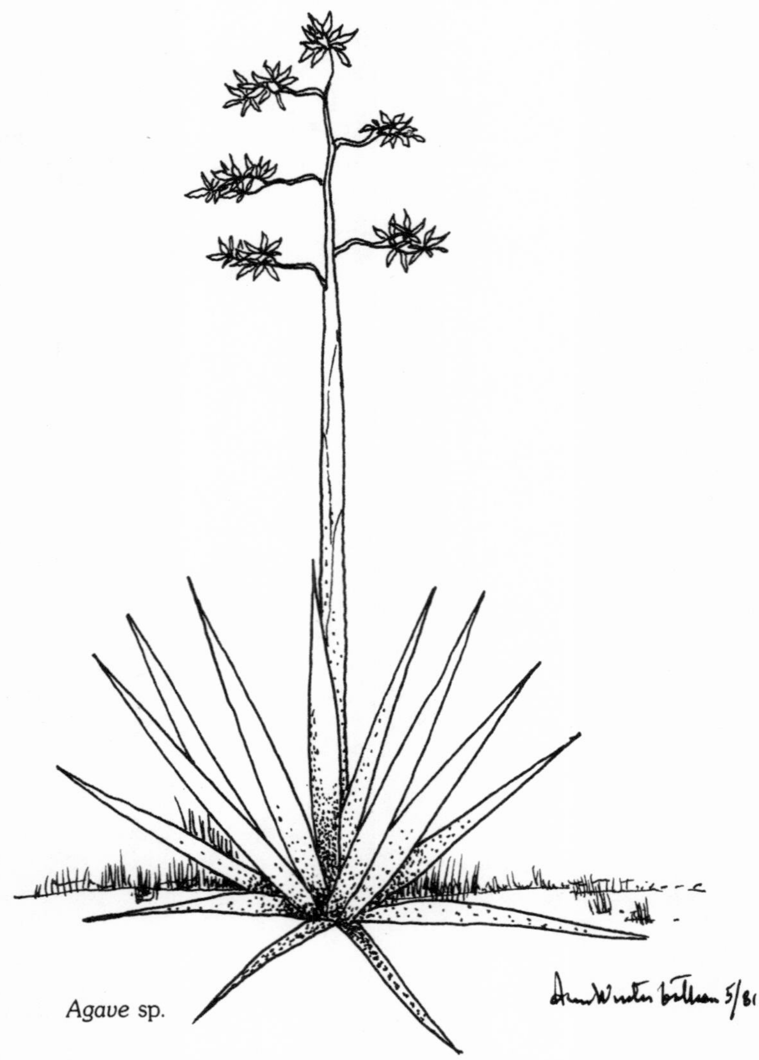

Agave sp.

MOST COMMON NAME: CENTURY PLANT

WHERE FOUND

Many species introduced and very common in garden plantings and well-drained, dry wild places.

Agave decipiens may be native, may have been introduced in prehistoric times by aboriginal man, or may be of more recent introduction—a puzzle yet to be deciphered.

COMMON NAMES	SCIENTIFIC NAME
CENTURY PLANT Sisal Maguey American "Aloe"	*Agave* spp. AMARYLLIDACEAE The DAFFODIL FAMILY (Some authors use AGAVACEAE, AGAVE FAMILY)

DESCRIPTION

Agavuos, Greek, meaning admirable; important cultivated plants of desert or well-drained regions; stem lacking, caudex present in some; stiff, fleshy leaves, often armed, persist for several years, grow in close rosette. Some species produce numerous flat black seeds from tall (often to 30′) inflorescence. Others produce bulbils or small well-developed plantlets from inflorescence. These shower down by the hundreds and provide ample new plants, for in most species the parent rosette dies after inflorescing. Plants may also reproduce from offsets of parent.

NATURE OF TOXICITY

A kind of saponin (a hepato-nephro-toxin in this case) and oxalic acid are present in the sap of some species.

SYMPTOMS

Dark-colored urine, liver and kidney damage (acute toxic hepatitis and nephritis). In animals some species of *Agave* cause coma and death. Juice causes extremely bothersome dermatitis lasting for many days. Dermatitis may be accompanied by hundreds of blisters.

FIRST AID

For dermatitis, wash thoroughly with Fels-Naptha bar soap; apply calamine. For other symptoms, seek emergency medical aid.

REMARKS

Plants of this genus are used to produce pulque, mescal and tequila. Also, starchy centers produced food for aboriginals of the American West. Care should be taken in any food experiments with Agaves. And as most are armed with a hard, sharp, terminal leaf thorn, it is well to amputate these terminal thorns as they appear.

Schinus terebinthifolius

MOST COMMON NAME: BRAZILIAN PEPPER

WHERE FOUND

Very common in almost all South Florida habitats. An aggressive, difficult-to-control exotic invader; very damaging to our wildlife habitats. Illegal to plant on Sanibel.

COMMON NAMES	SCIENTIFIC NAME
BRAZILIAN PEPPER Florida Holly Aroeira	*Schinus terebinthifolius* ANACARDIACEAE The CASHEW FAMILY

DESCRIPTION

Multiple-trunked tree, to 40′; creates impenetrable thickets; leaves from female plants aromatic, peppery or turpentine odor. Male plants lack odor. Leaves odd pinnate, usually 7, 9, 11, 13 leaflets, sometimes more; sometimes 5. Sometimes rachis and petiole winged. Leaves 2″ to 10″ or longer. Leaflets obovate, ovate, sometimes lanceolate. Terminal leaflets sometimes larger than laterals. Most leaflet margins are crenate-serrate. Some leaflets glabrous or with varying degrees of pilosity.

In its native Brazil, this species exists in five subspecies, four of which were introduced into the United States, one as early as 1842; others from Brazil, Algeria and a Paris seed dealer. It is believed that our Pepper trees are of very mixed ancestry which may account for their extreme vigor.

NATURE OF TOXICITY

The balsamic exudate from the trunk and stems contains cardol, resins, saponin, essential oils and tannins.

The fruits contain nine volatile monoterpene hydrocarbons which are the probable causes of human respiratory problems. More than 50 other compounds including sesquiterpenes, triterpenes, alcohols and ketones have been found. The seeds contain a large quantity of an essential oil composed principally of phellandrene plus a green aromatic fatty oil.

SYMPTOMS

When handling, cutting, trimming this tree, some people get a tormenting itching rash. Eye swelling and extreme discomfort is often present. Respiratory asthma-like problems are frequently severe. Fruits, when eaten, cause gastroenteritis, diarrhea, vomiting.

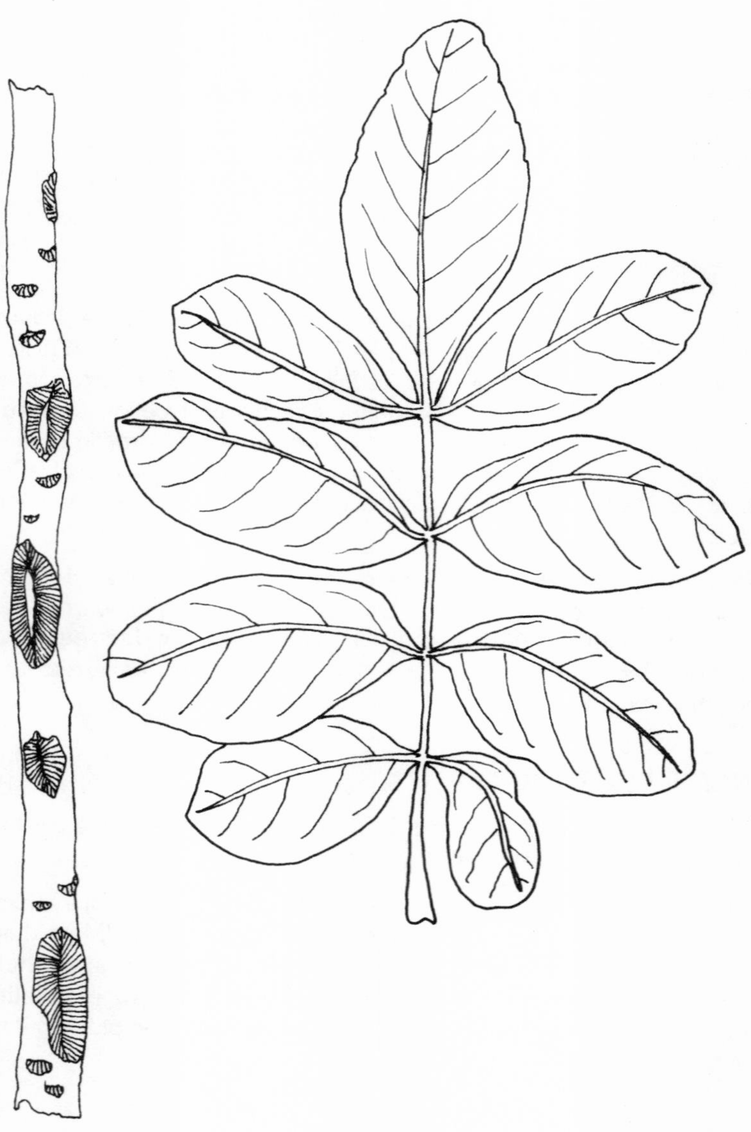

Schinus terebinthifolius is notably polymorphic. Note how very different this specimen from Hendry County is from specimen shown on page 22. There are literally dozens of different morphs growing in Florida. Drawing at left shows evidence of disease on stem.

FIRST AID

Wash sap from skin after handling, using Fels-Naptha bar soap. Calamine lotion can be of assistance. Seek medical aid if serious.

REMARKS

Avoid handling any part of this tree. Eradicate from your property. Avoid "imported pink peppercorns" in gourmet shops since this consists of *Schinus* fruits.

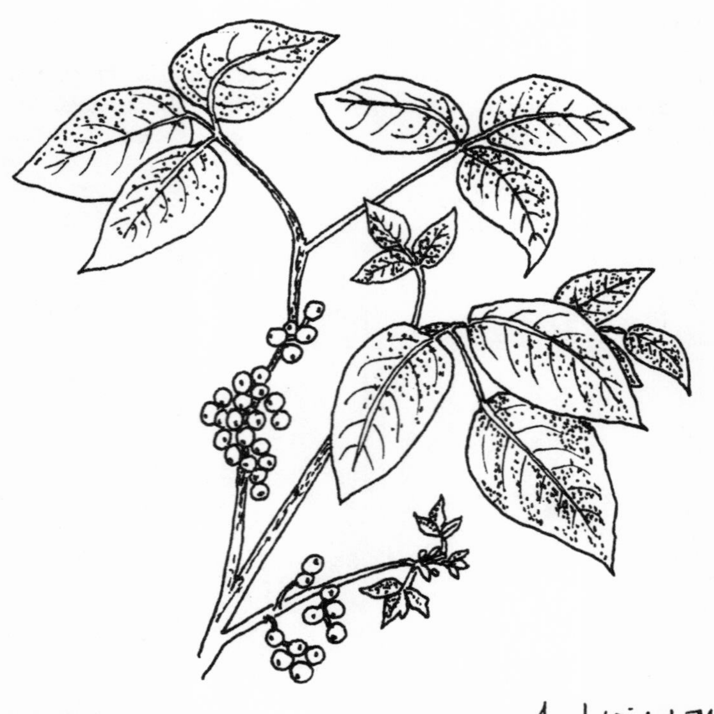

Rhus toxicodendron

MOST COMMON NAME: POISON IVY

WHERE FOUND

All forested areas; especially abundant on Sabal Palms.

COMMON NAME	SCIENTIFIC NAMES
POISON IVY	*Toxicodendron radicans* (Syn) *Rhus toxicodendron*
	ANACARDIACEAE The CASHEW FAMILY

DESCRIPTION

A beautiful, shiny alternate tri-compound leafed vine, sometimes a free-standing low shrub. Leaves green spring and summer; red, yellow-orange fall and winter. Flowers tiny white or green with 5 petals; fruit white, round, to 1/4″ diameter, waxy, utilized by birds, which distribute viable seed. In Florida, Poison Ivy is very common. Most Sabal Palms and many trees and bushes bear this beautiful but toxic plant. A few have been observed with 3″ diameter stems.

NATURE OF TOXICITY

All parts contain the phenolic substance once called urushiol, now identified as 3-n-penta-decylcatechol. It is a poison to the GI tract and very irritating to the skin. It will contaminate and maintain its toxicity for long periods in or on shoes or clothing.

SYMPTOMS

Itching and burning are early symptoms (and may be delayed up to four or five days after exposure). Facial swelling, blisters, inflammation are common. Even those who feel themselves immune are sometimes affected, for a delayed hypersensitivity reaction sometimes manifests itself after repeated exposures. Often first or early exposures do not result in the characteristic skin reaction. Breathing smoke from burning plants can cause special irritation.

FIRST AID

Wash with Fels-Naptha bar soap. Apply calamine lotion, seek medical aid.

REMARKS

Members of Anacardiaceae are all suspect. Poison wood, Mango, Brazilian Pepper, Cashew, Pistachio—all pertain to this family.

Local Poison Ivy is somewhat different in appearance from northern plants of the same species—enough so, at least, to confuse northern visitors who sometimes experience difficulty in recognizing it.

Allamanda cathartica

MOST COMMON NAME: YELLOW ALLAMANDA

WHERE FOUND

Disturbed areas and under cultivation.

COMMON NAME	SCIENTIFIC NAME
YELLOW ALLAMANDA	*Allamanda cathartica*
	APOCYNACEAE The OLEANDER FAMILY

DESCRIPTION

Shrub or vining shrub to 10–12′ tall; yellow flowers, showy, funnelform. Leaves $2^1/_2$″–5″, in whorls usually of 4, elliptic, undulate margins, short acuminate (tapering gradually to a pointed apex). Fruit two-valved, soft poisonous capsule containing winged seeds.

NATURE OF TOXICITY

Capsule containing concentrated poisonous purgative, but all parts toxic. Exact nature of toxic agents not determined.

SYMPTOMS

Dermal itching and eruptions from contact with the latex sap. A strong purgative. Has been used as an anthelmintic in folk medicine in Asia and in Latin America.

FIRST AID

Induce vomiting if ingested. If exposure is topical, wash with Fels-Naptha bar soap. Seek emergency medical aid.

REMARKS

A popular, beautiful plant that, though toxic, causes few problems. We do not suggest elimination, but urge planting away from doors or windows where frequent pruning will not be required.

Catharanthus roseus

A. Winterbotham

MOST COMMON NAME: PERIWINKLE

WHERE FOUND

Gardens; disturbed sites; roadsides

COMMON NAMES	SCIENTIFIC NAMES
PERIWINKLE Madagascar Periwinkle Old Maid Bright Eyes	*Catharanthus roseus* formerly *Vinca rosea*, *Lochnera rosea*, and *Ammocallis rosea*
	APOCYNACEAE The OLEANDER FAMILY

DESCRIPTION

Herb or shrub, 10″ to 3′, even 4′. Leaves 1½″ to 3″ long; oblong, rounded at apex, narrows to short petiole at base, light-colored veining. Flowers pink, white, white with pink center, pink with deeper pink center, deep pink with white. Corolla tube cylindrical, stamens short, anthers attached almost directly to corolla tube.

NATURE OF TOXICITY

The oncolytic alkaloid vincristine (formerly leurocristine) is present in all parts of the plant. Commercially-prepared vincristine is used in the treatment of leukemia, Hodgkin's Disease, lymphosarcoma, and other malignancies. 500 kg. of *Catharanthus* are needed to produce 1 gm. of vincristine. A second oncolytic alkaloid, vinblastine, is also present, as are more than 50 others—this plant is really a factory of alkaloids, many of which are not yet completely studied.

SYMPTOMS

Uric acid nephropathy, preexisting neuromuscular disease aggravated neurologically, hair loss, paralytic ileus may occur as side effects of drug administration. It is probable that these symptoms would not appear from the accidental or incidental ingestion of the plant or its parts due to the low concentration of the alkaloids present in the living plant, but knowledge of this multiple alkaloid-producer and care in handling are in order.

Catharanthus roseus showing bud just below the flower. Seed pods are shown at each of the lower nodes.

FIRST AID

Induce vomiting, seek emergency medical aid.

REMARKS

This common and much-loved plant probably does not constitute a serious hazard. However children should be encouraged to leave it alone and not put it in the mouth.

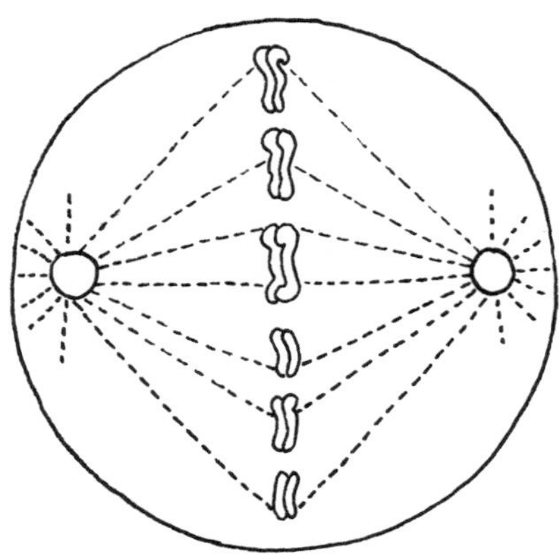

This is the metaphase stage of cell division, here hypothetically represented. This is the stage which vincristine interrupts. Note chromosomes, beginning to divide, arranged on the cell's equator.

—After Dorland

Ervatamia coronaria

MOST COMMON NAME: CRAPE JASMINE

WHERE FOUND

In gardens. Introduced from India.

COMMON NAMES	SCIENTIFIC NAME
CRAPE JASMINE Crape Jessamine East Indian Rose Bay Nero's Crown	*Ervatamia coronaria* APOCYNACEAE The OLEANDER FAMILY

DESCRIPTION

Shrub to seven feet tall; leaves undulate, dark shiny green, pointed, 5″–7″; flowers 2″ in diameter; white waxy ruffled edges, clustered, fragrant undulate petals. Fruits have orange-colored pods but are seldom seen. Probably native to India where wood is burned as incense and also used in folk medicine.

NATURE OF TOXICITY

Stem and roots concentrate alkaloids including coronarine and others not completely identified. Flowers produce a substance that has corticosteroid properties.

SYMPTOMS

White milky sap can cause dermatitis. In its native India it and others of its genus have caused death after ingestion. No such cases are known here. The plant seldom fruits here.

FIRST AID

For dermatitis, flush thoroughly, wash in Fels-Naptha bar soap and water. Seek emergency medical aid.

REMARKS

A beautiful exotic, commonly grown. Certainly safe to plant with minimum precautions.

Nerium oleander

MOST COMMON NAME: OLEANDER

WHERE FOUND

Gardens, roadside plantings. Persists in old, once inhabited areas.

COMMON NAME	SCIENTIFIC NAME
OLEANDER Rose Bay	*Nerium oleander*
	APOCYNACEAE The OLEANDER FAMILY

DESCRIPTION

Popular shrub or small tree to 20 feet, with whorled, usually opposite or in whorls of threes (ternate) leathery (coriaceous) lanceolate or thin ovate 2½″–5″ leaves. Flowers single or double; showy white, crimson or rose-purple. Scent sweet, pleasant, but reminiscent of cheap perfume. Old plants often ugly with much dead wood. Seed pod to 6″ long, opening longitudinally revealing packed slender, winged seeds.

NATURE OF TOXICITY

The leaves, flowers, stems, seeds, roots all contain toxic glycosides among which are the important agents, neriin (nerioside) and oleandrin (oleandroside) which resemble digitoxin in action.

SYMPTOMS

Vomiting, abdominal cramps, diarrhea, drowsiness, lowered pulse, internal bleeding, visual blurring, enlarged pupils and vertigo are a few of the symptoms of ingestion; loss of consciousness and even death may result in severe cases.

FIRST AID

Seek immediate emergency medical aid. Retain specimens of vomitus and plant consumed, if possible, for positive identification.

REMARKS

This native of the Mediterranean Basin is a plant known to be dangerous since classical times and is mentioned by Pliny and Galen, among others.

When the writer was a schoolboy in Florida, a fellow student used a *Nerium* twig to roast marshmallows. He died. Smoke from fires where *Nerium* trash is burned can cause serious poisoning. Oleander honey is poisonous.

Dieffenbachia sp.

MOST COMMON NAME: *DIEFFENBACHIA*

WHERE FOUND

Houses, patios, outside gardens, grocery stores, florist shops, doctors' offices.

COMMON NAMES	SCIENTIFIC NAME
DIEFFENBACHIA Dumb Cane Conmigo Ninguem Pode	*Dieffenbachia spp.* ARACEAE The ARUM FAMILY

DESCRIPTION

A popular houseplant found in commerce throughout the USA. Herbaceous, it has thick leaves and stem; flower typically aroid, like Jack-in-the-Pulpit. There are many cultivars: some with almost solid green leaves, others with almost white or ivory leaves. There are all gradations and patterns of green and white in others. Leaves may be from a few inches to over a foot long. A large plant may be 12′ to 15′ tall. Most are 1′–2′.

NATURE OF TOXICITY

The juice of the stem, leaf and root is highly irritating. The active principles are thought to be calcium oxalate and protoanemonine. The former, when found in stem only (not leaf), causes severe irritation of mucosa (mouth, throat, intestines, stomach); the latter causes swelling of the air passages and may be fatal. Toxins other than the above are probably responsible for nausea, vomiting and diarrhea. Numerous serious cases of Dumb Cane poisoning are recorded, both in the United States and in the plant's native Brazil.

SYMPTOMS

Irritation, salivation, swelling, difficulty in breathing, nausea, vomiting, death from strangulation. Thought to cause sterility. Amerindians use the juice as an arrow poison: victim suffers swelling and inflammation. Repotting and cutting may cause serious hand and arm inflammation. May render victim unable to speak, hence "Dumb" Cane. History records illiterate servants rendered dumb by the employment of this plant to preserve secrecy.

FIRST AID

Flush affected skin with water. Wash with Fels-Naptha bar soap. If larynx and pharynx affected and breathing difficult, seek to maintain open air passages and get medical attention promptly.

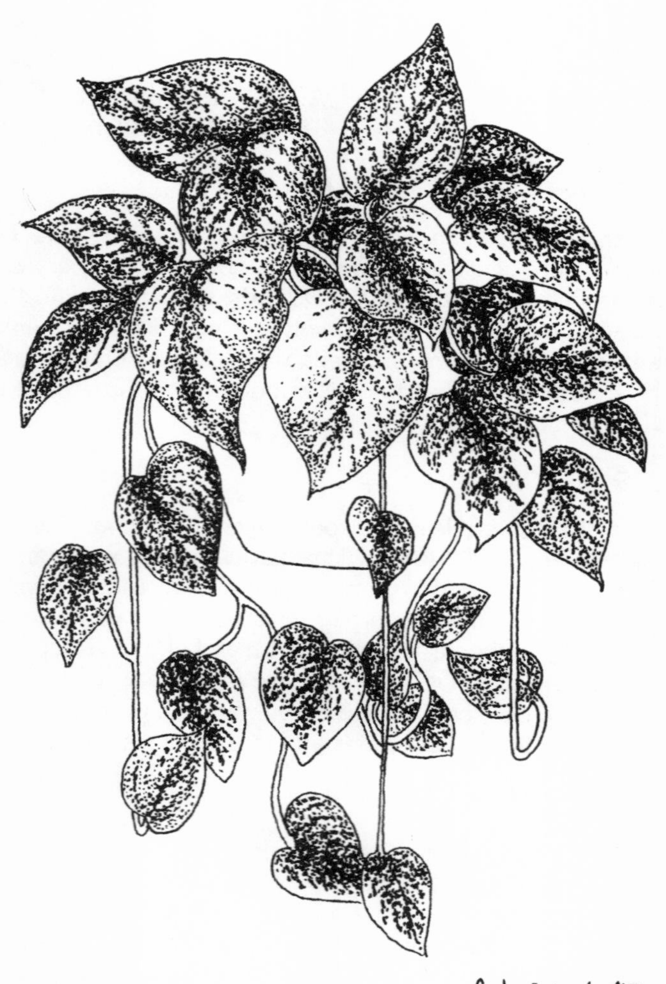

Rhaphidophora aurea A. Winterbotham

MOST COMMON NAME: POTHOS

WHERE FOUND

Gardens, patios, hanging baskets, palm trunks.

COMMON NAMES	SCIENTIFIC NAMES
POTHOS Hunter's Robe Mistakenly called Philodendron	Rhaphidophora aurea (formerly *Pothos aureus*) ARACEAE The ARUM FAMILY

DESCRIPTION

A beautiful green, yellow and white-patterned split-leafed vining aroid. Leaves large, oval or heart-shaped, to 2′ when climbing a palm; heavy 1″–2″ diameter stem. Much smaller leaves (2″–4″) when potted or creeping on the ground. Flowers inconspicuous: Jack-in-the-Pulpit-like. Some palm trunks are completely hidden by the heavy growth of this vine.

NATURE OF TOXICITY

Sap contains calcium oxalate and is very irritating to mouth, throat, stomach and intestines if swallowed or chewed.

SYMPTOMS

Temporary loss of speech, swelling of the throat, diarrhea are common symptoms, as are burning and irritation of hands and arms in cases where the plant is handled, cut or repotted.

FIRST AID

Wash exposed skin with Fels-Naptha bar soap. Seek medical attention promptly.

REMARKS

Many aroids (most *Philodendron* spp., *Alocasia* spp. and the many "elephant ears," *Xanthosoma* spp.) are similarly toxic. Commonly sold in nurseries for outside planting and in florist departments of supermarkets for indoor or porch hanging baskets.

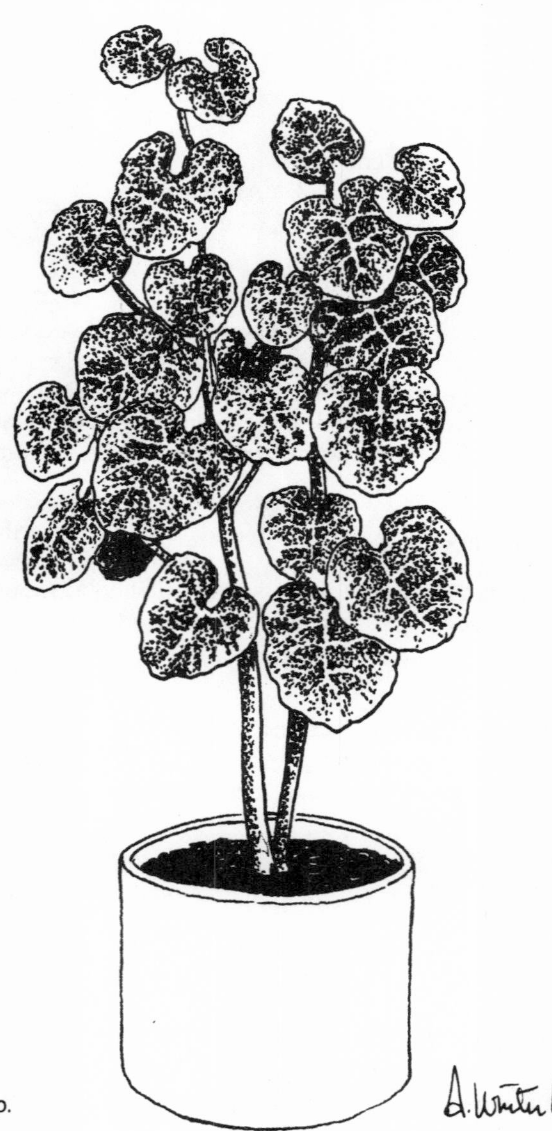

Polyscias sp.

MOST COMMON NAME: ARALIA

WHERE FOUND

Exotic cultivars planted in many gardens

COMMON NAME	SCIENTIFIC NAME
ARALIA	*Polyscias spp.*
	ARALIACEAE The GINSENG FAMILY

DESCRIPTION

Shrubs or low trees. Usually variegated odd pinnate compound leaves. There are many varieties, some with finely "cut" leaves, centers with white-patched, pink-margined, irregular tooth-edged leaflets. Flowers rarely seen.

NATURE OF TOXICITY

The sap is a skin irritant. Workers who trim or cultivate these plants often have rash or sores. If you must have Aralias, plant them away from regularly-used paths. Believed to contain irritating saponins.

SYMPTOMS

Chewing on the leaves has caused children to have rash and sores around the mouth, and also difficulty in swallowing.

FIRST AID

Wash with Fels-Naptha bar soap.

Cryptostegia grandiflora

MOST COMMON NAME: RUBBER VINE

WHERE FOUND

Gardens. Escaped and naturalized in a few places.

COMMON NAMES	SCIENTIFIC NAME
RUBBER VINE Purple "Allamanda" Pink "Allamanda"	*Cryptostegia grandiflora* ASCLEPIADACEAE The MILKWEED FAMILY

DESCRIPTION

Thick-stemmed, woody vine; broad, leathery oval leaves 5″–6″ long. Cultivated and popular as an ornamental. Flowers are conspicuous and funnelform, purple or pink, sometimes white. Twisted in the bud. Milky sap contains latex. Origin disputed: some authorities believe it native to Africa, others to India.

NATURE OF TOXICITY

Plant produces a cardiac glycoside. Its similarity to digitoxin has been noted. All parts (root, stem, leaves, flowers) are highly toxic.

SYMPTOMS

Severe gastroenteritis and bloody diarrhea result from ingestion of even small quantities of the sap. Handling *Cryptostegia* trash can cause severe irritation to the airways and eyes. Labored, painful breathing can result. There are records of fatalities.

FIRST AID

For problems resulting from ingestion, seek medical aid promptly. For topical exposure, wash well with yellow laundry soap. Flush eyes with water; seek medical aid.

REMARKS

Thomas Edison, in his effort to free the United States from foreign natural rubber dependence, studied this and many other plants that produce latex. This plant may have been introduced to Florida by Edison.

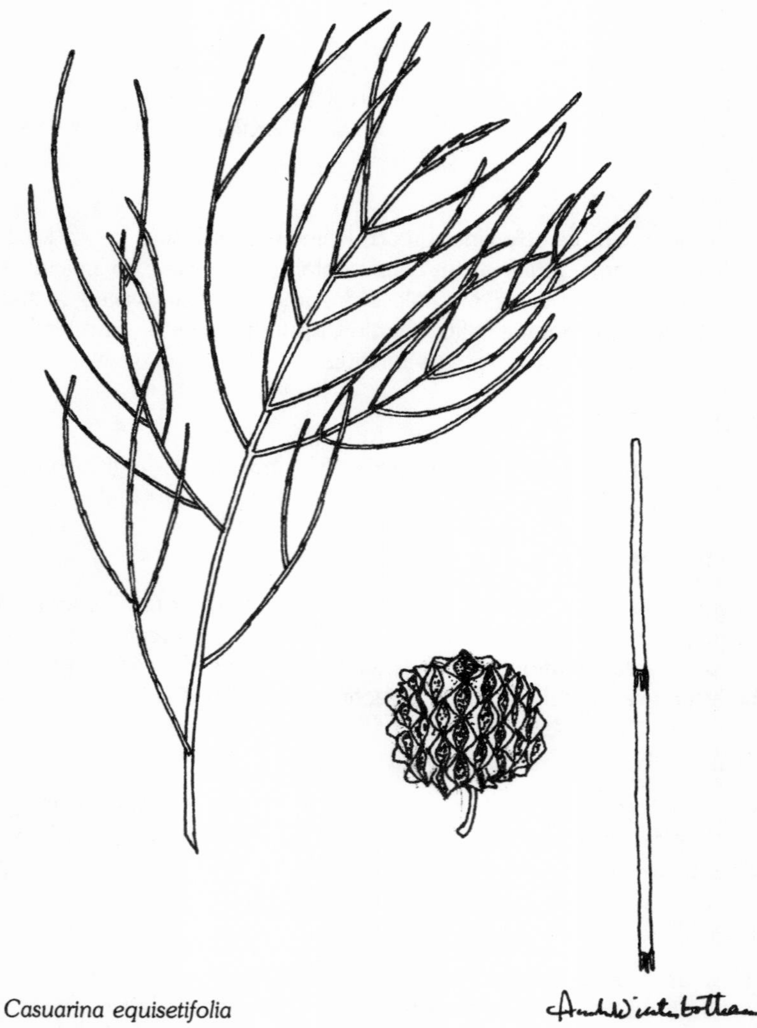

Casuarina equisetifolia

MOST COMMON NAME: AUSTRALIAN "PINE"

WHERE FOUND

Still planted in some gardens; escaped exuberantly to all habitats except Mangrove and lowland wetlands. The most prominent large plants of South Florida's coastal areas.

COMMON NAMES	SCIENTIFIC NAME
AUSTRALIAN "PINE"	*Casuarina equisetifolia*
Casuarina	and related species
She Oak	
Beefwood	CASUARINACEAE
Horse-Tail Tree	The BEEFWOOD FAMILY

DESCRIPTION

The name is from *Casuarius,* the ostrich-like bird whose plumage is (superficially) like the branches of *Casuarina.* Jointed and almost leafless, they resemble equisetums. Leaves or teeth are reduced and are the almost whorled points seen when joints are separated.

NATURE OF TOXICITY

"Farmers Lung" (Extrinsic Allergic Alveolitis, also called allergic pneumonia) results from inhaling certain dusts from sources such as moldy hay, cheese fungus, grain flour and *Casuarina* duff. Resultant immune complex concentrates and deposits in the lungs where lung damage which may include edema, thrombosis and hemorrhage may occur.

SYMPTOMS

Fever, chills, dyspnea (difficult breathing), cough, tightness of chest, inspiratory crepitations (crackling sounds when inhaling).

FIRST AID

Quickly seek emergency medical aid. Sample of presumed causative duff or dust can be collected in a plastic bag. Suggest O_2 if in acute pneumonia-like stage.

REMARKS

If you are one who suffers from *Casuarina* problems, we suggest you not work with *Casuarina* duff or mulch. We also suggest that existing trees be removed from the properties of sensitive people. Other vegetation mulches or dusts may cause this condition. I am indebted to Dr. Stephan Halabis of Sanibel for help in this area.

Casuarina is listed in Lewis and Lewis's *Medical Botany* as an aeroallergen causing hay fever, bronchial asthma, and/or hypersensitivity pneumonitis.

Rhoea spathacea

MOST COMMON NAME: OYSTER PLANT

WHERE FOUND

Gardens, patios, sometimes seen as naturalized escapee in old once-inhabited locations.

COMMON NAMES	SCIENTIFIC NAME
OYSTER PLANT Moses Plant Boat "Lily"	*Rhoea spathacea* (or *R. discolor*) COMMELINACEAE The SPIDERWORT FAMILY

DESCRIPTION

A short-stemmed plant with long, brittle, juicy leaves. Leaves form rosette not unlike a small *Agave*. Flowers many, white and small, growing in an oyster- or boat-shaped structure growing from leaf axil. Three varieties common in Florida: large (probably var. *vittata*) with leaves 8–12 inches long, green above, purple beneath; a similar variety, *varigata*, with yellow stripes above and a small, pygmy form, green and purple.

NATURE OF TOXICITY

The nature of the irritating factor in the juice seems not to have been identified.

SYMPTOMS

Itching dermatitis and skin eruptions. Can cause difficulty in breathing. Mouth irritation results when leaves are chewed.

FIRST AID

Wash exposed skin with Fels-Naptha bar soap and water.

REMARKS

This commonly-used ornamental is not of great public health significance, but care should be exercised in handling and transplanting this tropical American native.

Setcreasea purpurea A. Winterbotham

MOST COMMON NAME: PURPLE QUEEN

WHERE FOUND

Gardens, pots, patios, hanging baskets.

COMMON NAME	SCIENTIFIC NAME
PURPLE QUEEN	*Setcreasea purpurea*
	COMMELINACEAE The SPIDERWORT FAMILY

DESCRIPTION

A purple, brittle-stemmed, turgid, juicy herb; fragile juicy purple leaves; flowers lavender or pink, growing from a pair of purple bracts; stem 1/4″. This Mexican plant is commonly used in landscaping in South Florida.

NATURE OF TOXICITY

Juice contains irritating principle, chemical identification of which is unknown.

SYMPTOMS

Dermatitis, itching, rash.

FIRST AID

Wash in Fels-Naptha bar soap and water.

REMARKS

The writer introduced it to the Bahamas where it is widely planted today.

Momordica charantia

MOST COMMON NAME: WILD BALSAM APPLE

WHERE FOUND

In many disturbed areas.

COMMON NAMES	SCIENTIFIC NAME
WILD BALSAM APPLE	*Momordica charantia*
Wild Cucumber	
Bitter Gourd	CUCURBITACEAE
Balsam Pear	The GOURD FAMILY
Cerasee	

DESCRIPTION

Prostrate or climbing vine, sometimes annual, may be perennial; herbaceous with tendrils which may branch. Flowers unisexual, male flowers clustered, female solitary yellow. Leaves palmately lobed (5–7). Fruit, a berry $^3/_4''$ to $2''$ long, yellow or orange, oblong rough exterior. Ripe fruit splits open and inverts in three parts, exposing seeds covered by red arils. (Arils *only* are sweet and edible).

NATURE OF TOXICITY

Seeds are highly toxic, bitter, purgative; contain the toxin momordicin. The orange fruit contains a hypoglycemic agent, charantin, which, when ingested, causes a little reduction in blood sugar but it has not proved useful in the management of diabetes in animals. It did cause uterine hemorrhage. In developing countries, sometimes used as an abortifacient. Leaves may be boiled in three waters and safely eaten. Cultivated in Asia and eaten in *unripe* state.

SYMPTOMS

Vomiting, diarrhea, stomach ache, general malaise which may last several days. May cause illness after only a small quantity of either seed or fruit is consumed.

FIRST AID

Induce vomiting. Seek emergency medical aid.

REMARKS

Although aril and leaves are edible, our advice is to leave this plant alone.

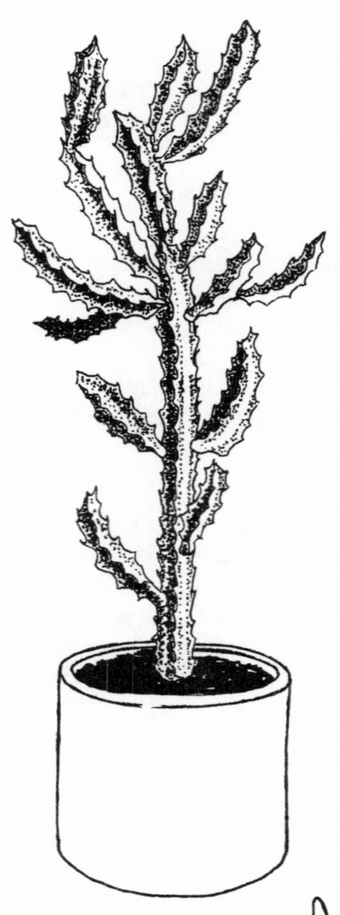

Euphorbia lactea

MOST COMMON NAME: CANDELABRA "CACTUS"

WHERE FOUND

Commonly planted in gardens; popular as potted plant. Frequently seen amongst cacti in florist shops and nurseries and sold as a cactus.

COMMON NAMES	SCIENTIFIC NAME
CANDELABRA "CACTUS" Dragon-Bone Tree	*Euphorbia lactea* EUPHORBIACEAE The SPURGE FAMILY

DESCRIPTION

Spiny, succulent, cactus-like Asian ornamental. Fleshy, spiny, triangular stems; green, sometimes with white blotched pattern; branched; produces minute inconspicuous leaves. Best distinguished from a true cactus by presence of white sap which may be revealed with a knifepoint. There are several cultivars, most prized of which is the popular *E. lactea* var. "Christata," called Elkhorn or Frilled Fan, a thick, curled, spiny, abnormal-looking growth with fan-like extremities.

NATURE OF TOXICITY

Milky sap is extremely caustic topically and if ingested is very irritating to the GI tract and is a strong purgative. See general comments on co-carcinogens on page 5.

SYMPTOMS

Painful dermatitis consisting of swelling and blisters may result from exposure to the sap. If the sap spatters into the eyes it may cause temporary blindness, acute keratoconjunctivitis accompanied by pain and swelling eyelids. While victims recover, the experience is painful in the extreme.

FIRST AID

If ingested, induce vomiting. If problem is topical, wash thoroughly with Fels-Naptha bar soap. If sap is in the eyes, flush copiously with water; urgently seek emergency medical aid.

REMARKS

We suggest that this plant be extirpated from gardens. Unfortunately it grows very well in our climate on our impoverished soils and is so popular that this suggestion is likely to be ignored, even though many much more attractive non-toxic true cacti are available and grow vigorously here.

Euphorbia splendens

MOST COMMON NAME: CROWN OF THORNS

WHERE FOUND

This popular plant, native to Madagascar, is found in hundreds of gardens.

COMMON NAME	SCIENTIFIC NAMES
CROWN OF THORNS	*Euphorbia milii* (Syn) *E. splendens*
	EUPHORBIACEAE The SPURGE FAMILY

DESCRIPTION

Flowers usually bright red in long-stalked clusters; pink as well as the common coral cultivars are now seen. A low-growing, excessively-thorny plant. Stem $^1/_2$″ thick with numerous half-inch thorns. Leaves entire, obovate, few. Milky sap.

NATURE OF TOXICITY

The white sap contains toxic agents which are irritating. Recent work by Hecker et al. would indicate this species not to be co-carcinogenic.

SYMPTOMS

The milky sap is caustic and frequently causes painful dermatitis on contact. It causes severe irritation of mucosa of the GI tract when put in the mouth and swallowed, accompanied by vomiting, burning pain and diarrhea. Painful, though temporary, blindness occurs if sap is inadvertently rubbed in the eyes.

FIRST AID

Flush areas of exposure with water. Cause vomiting if ingested. Seek emergency medical aid.

REMARKS

Sap has been used as a purgative.

If the plant is native to Madagascar, the popular myth that it was Jesus' Crown of Thorns can hardly be given credence.

Euphorbia pulcherrima A. Winterbotham

MOST COMMON NAME: POINSETTIA

WHERE FOUND

Heavily traded by florists at Christmas. Often planted in the ground.

COMMON NAMES	SCIENTIFIC NAME
POINSETTIA Christmas Flower Christmas Rose	*Euphorbia pulcherrima* EUPHORBEACEAE The SPURGE FAMILY

DESCRIPTION

In pots, 1′–4′; planted out, a shrub or tree growing to 15′. Those 6″–8″ leaves around inconspicuous flowers are green, yellow, scarlet or (in some cultivars) white, cream or pink. Basis of a huge wintertime industry, this Mexican plant is now thought not to offer hazards to gardeners, pets or children. However, the final score is not in, so this writer suggests caution.

NATURE OF TOXICITY

Milky sap may be caustic; if ingested, may be irritating to the GI tract and is thought to be purgative. Stoller, in Boston, reports many Christmastime problems with this plant. Hecker, in Heidelberg, believes this plant to offer no co-carcinogenic problem.

SYMPTOMS

Dermatitis has been recorded due to exposure to the sap. If the sap spatters into the eyes it may cause painful irritation and keratoconjunctivitis accompanied by swelling of eyelids.

FIRST AID

If ingested, induce vomiting. If problem is topical, wash with Fels-Naptha bar soap. If sap is in the eyes, wash with water copiously and seek emergency medical aid if irritation persists.

REMARKS

There are three wild poinsettias in Florida readily recognizable by white sap and upper leaves blotched with red or white; to 3′, some with linear-lanceolate leaves (*Poinsettia pinetorum*) and *P. cyathophora,* with lobed, mostly oblong leaves. *P. heterophylla,* Painted Leaf, has very polymorphic leaves. Flowers of these species are cup-shaped like *pulcherrima.* The toxicity of these species has not been studied.

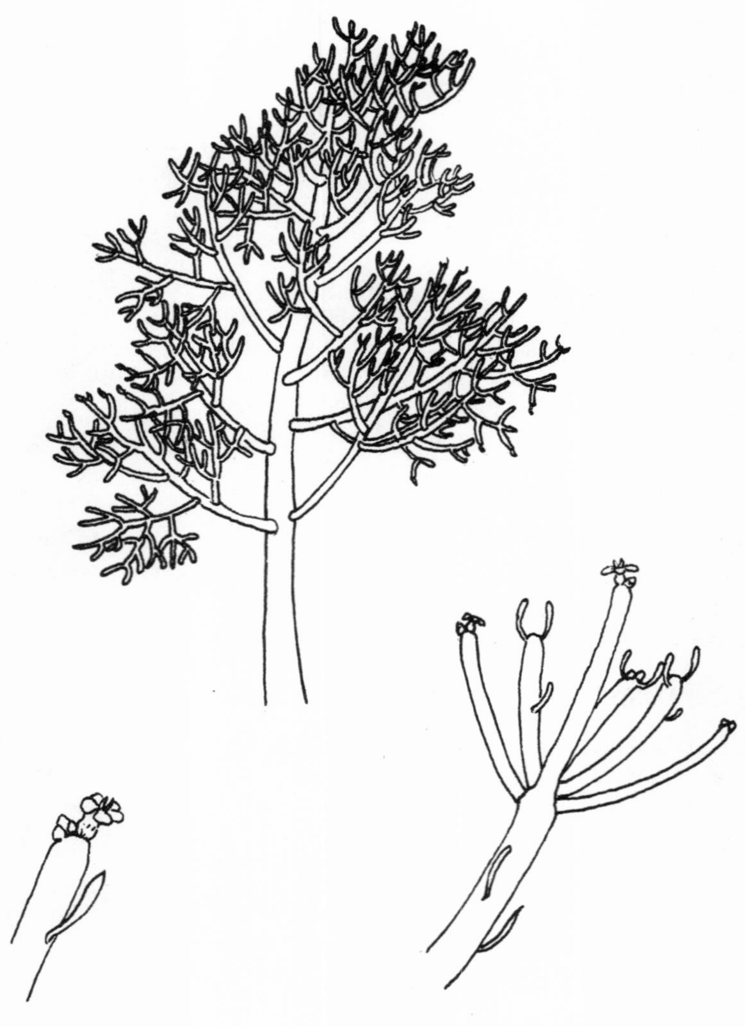

Euphorbia tirucalli

A. Winterbotham

MOST COMMON NAME: PENCIL TREE

WHERE FOUND

Many gardens. Also escaped and naturalized in many south Florida areas.

COMMON NAMES	SCIENTIFIC NAME
PENCIL TREE Monkey Puzzle Tree Milk Tree	*Euphorbia tirucalli* EUPHORBIACEAE The SPURGE FAMILY

DESCRIPTION

Usually seen as small tree to 10′, but may grow to 30′. Leaves are present but narrow and inconspicuous. Branches and numerous branchlets are shiny green and full of toxic milky sap. Trunks of old trees are not green but gray, with rough bark. Impenetrable; dangerous living fence in its native Africa. Grows profusely and needs frequent pruning in gardens. Those who plant or prune this tree must take care to protect themselves from the milky sap.

NATURE OF TOXICITY

Milky sap is extremely caustic and if ingested is very irritating to the GI tract, and is a strong purgative. This plant may be co-carcinogenic. See general comments on co-carcinogenicity on page 5.

SYMPTOMS

Painful dermatitis consisting of swelling and blisters results from exposure to the sap. If the sap spatters into the eyes, it may cause temporary blindness, acute keratoconjunctivitis accompanied by pain and swelling of eyelids. While victims recover, the experience is painful and fearful.

FIRST AID

If ingested, induce vomiting. If problem is topical, wash thoroughly with Fels-Naptha bar soap. If sap is in the eyes, wash copiously and urgently seek emergency medical aid.

REMARKS

We suggest that this plant be extirpated from gardens. Unfortunately it grows very well in our climate on our impoverished soils.

Jatropha multifida

MOST COMMON NAME: CORAL TREE

WHERE FOUND

Commonly planted in gardens and patios.

COMMON NAMES	SCIENTIFIC NAME
CORAL TREE Coral Plant Wrongly called "Nutmeg" Tree	*Jatropha multifida* EUPHORBIACEAE The SPURGE FAMILY

DESCRIPTION

A tree that grows to 20′ but usually seen at 3′ or 4′ to 7′ or 8′; 7 to 12 palmate leaf lobes to 1′ in size. Inflorescence resembles Mediterranean precious coral: pink-orange flower and stems, five-petaled flowers, yellow stamens. Three-seeded fruit yellow when ripe. Deciduous: loses all leaves in winter.

NATURE OF TOXICITY

Sticky sap, *not* white, as in many toxic members of family Euphorbiaceae, but yellow; contains jatrophin or curcin. More concentrated in seeds which are attractive and sometimes eaten by children. Fatalities are known. Curcin is similar to the toxic agent in Castor beans. Seeds contain an oil more purgative than castor oil. *Jatropha* may be co-carcinogenic. See general comments on co-carcinogens on page 5.

SYMPTOMS

Diarrhea, vomiting, gastroenteritis, impaired vision, fever, convulsions.

FIRST AID

Induce vomiting, if not already occurring. Seek emergency medical help.

REMARKS

Other members of genus *Jatropha* which are planted in Florida: *J. curas*, Physic Nut: *J. gossypifolia*, Bellyache Bush, cause similar problems.

Ricinus communis

MOST COMMON NAME: CASTOR BEAN

WHERE FOUND

Widely cultivated in Florida early in this century. It is now naturalized in hundreds of oldfields and other disturbed areas.

COMMON NAMES	SCIENTIFIC NAME
CASTOR BEAN Palma-Christi	*Ricinus communis*
	EUPHORBIACEAE The SPURGE FAMILY

DESCRIPTION

Shrub or tree growing to 30′–35′ but usually under 10′. Leaves peltate, palmately lobed (star-shaped), 8–10 lobes; leaves green, red or purple with red veins. Flower apetalous and inconspicuous; fruits borne in spikes to 2′ long, green, blue or beautiful red in some varieties. Each soft, spiny fruit capsule contains three colorful, patterned seeds. Each seed looks like a fat, well-fed tick. Linnaeus chose the generic name *Ricinus* which means "tick" in Latin. Seeds are tasty and attractive to children.

NATURE OF TOXICITY

Seeds may be pressed to secure the familiar purgative, castor oil, which is also used as an instrument lubricant. The "cake" remaining after the oil is pressed contains a toxalbumin called ricin. As if oil and ricin were not enough, Castor beans also contain a serious allergenic substance which may cause asthmatic breathing problems and dermal pustules and itching. Masticating and swallowing one seed can be fatal.

SYMPTOMS

Burning of abdomen, mouth and throat follows ingestion of seeds. Vomiting, persistent bloody diarrhea, fever, impaired vision, convulsions, anaphylactic shock occur. Many fatalities are recorded. Allergic responses as above.

FIRST AID

Induce vomiting for internal poisoning. Wash exposed skin with Fels-Naptha bar soap. Seek emergency medical aid.

REMARKS

There is risk in planting this species as an ornamental because of its extreme toxicity.

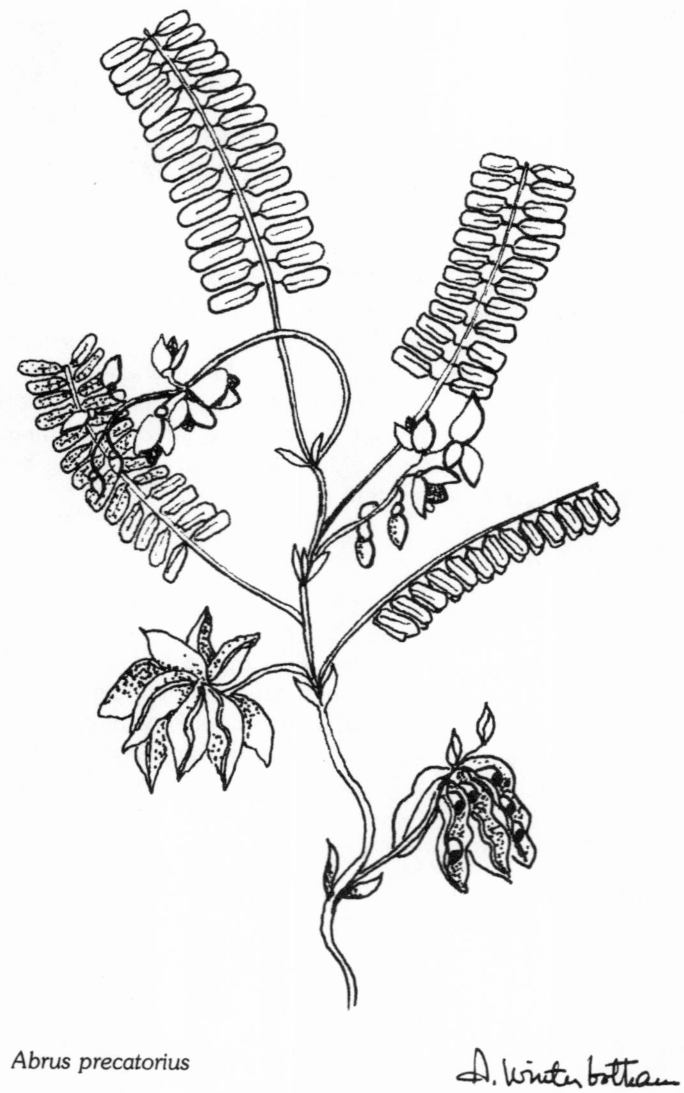

Abrus precatorius

MOST COMMON NAME: ROSARY PEA

WHERE FOUND

On Sabal Palms, shrubs, fences, disturbed areas.

COMMON NAMES

ROSARY PEA
Crab's Eye Vine
Weather Plant
Black Eyed Susan
Precatory Bean
Jequirity Bean

SCIENTIFIC NAME

Abrus precatorius

FABACEAE
(LEGUMINOSAE is alternate name)
The PEA FAMILY

DESCRIPTION

Small-stemmed vine; delicate, even pinnate compound leaves, 24–30; leaflets 1/2″ or smaller; flowers typically pea-like, 1/4″, white to lavender, sometimes pink; fruit clustered in up to 12 1″ pea pods, often 7 or 8. Seeds 3 to 6, sometimes 7, *scarlet* when *ripe*, hard, 3/16″ long, 1/4″ wide with *black spot* at point of connection to pod. Black spot conspicuous and about 20% of entire seed surface. Unripe seeds pink, larger, softer, easily strung as beads with needle and thread. The seeds are quite uniform and thus have been of use as carat weights in the gem trade in Asia where this plant is native.

NATURE OF TOXICITY

Seeds contain abrin. Kingsbury, in *Poisonous Plants of the U.S. and Canada* states abrin to be "one of the most potent toxic principles known." Less than one masticated seed can kill an adult human. Hard ripe seeds, when ingested but not masticated, usually pass harmlessly through the GI tract and are eliminated. Soft, unripe seeds are equally toxic and present a greater threat. When strung as beads, pricked fingers introduce abrin into the bloodstream. Severe illness results. William Burger, Chairman of Field Museum's Botany Department, stated abrin to be 1000 times as toxic as arsenic.

SYMPTOMS

One seed soft and unripe, or ripe and chewed, may be fatal. Abdominal pain, internal hemorrhage, vomiting, vertigo, bloody diarrhea, fast but weak heartbeat.

FIRST AID

Induce vomiting, seek immediate emergency medical aid. Take specimens for positive ID.

REMARKS

Plant should be eradicated.

Erythrina herbacea

MOST COMMON NAME: CHEROKEE BEAN

WHERE FOUND

Hammocks, coastal plains. Much sought after for garden planting.

COMMON NAMES	SCIENTIFIC NAMES
CHEROKEE BEAN Eastern Coral Bean Immortelle	*Erythrina herbacea* (Syn) *E. arborea* FABACEAE (LEGUMINOSAE is alternate name) The PEA FAMILY

DESCRIPTION

Shrub or tree to 30′; trunk, branches grey-green; armed, trifoliate compound leaves to 6″ or 7″; leaflets hastate or arrowhead-shaped to deltoid. Often prickly beneath on petiole and rachis. Inflorescence: one to several spike-like racemes with pea-like flowers arranged along long axis; long broad erect petal to about $^1/_2$″, scarlet. Fruit, like bean pod, to 6″ long. Seeds brilliant scarlet; cling to pod after it splits open. Perennial, growing huge, to 2′ diameter underground tuber. In northern part of its range, above-ground parts die back in winter.

NATURE OF TOXICITY

The lovely red seeds contain six deadly alkaloids: erysodine, erysopine, erysovine, ersothropine, erysothiovine, hypophorine. Ground seeds mixed with peanut butter have been used for rat poison. New leaves and flowers are sometimes cooked and eaten but we advise against this bucolic practice.

SYMPTOMS

Central nervous system depressant; dizziness.

FIRST AID

Seek emergency medical aid. Take any available specimens.

REMARKS

Other members of genus *Erythrina* are sometimes brought to Florida and planted. All *Erythrina* spp. are thought to have toxic seeds.

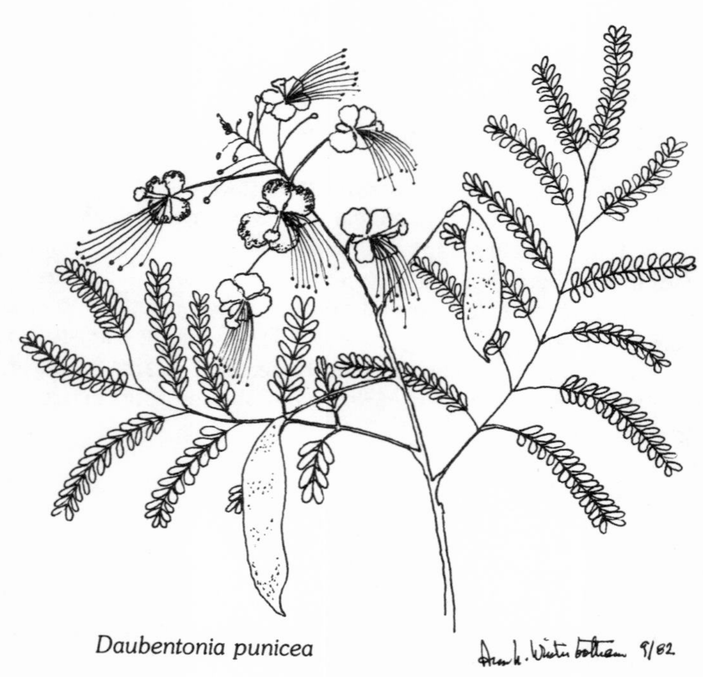

Daubentonia punicea

MOST COMMON NAME: DWARF POINCIANA

WHERE FOUND

Gardens. A popular ornamental.

COMMON NAMES	SCIENTIFIC NAMES
DWARF POINCIANA False Poinciana Rattlebox Sesbane	*Sesbania punicea* Syn. *Daubentonia punicea*
	FABACEAE (LEGUMINOSAE is alternate name) The PEA FAMILY

DESCRIPTION

Shrub or tree to 10′ tall. Leaves 6″ to 10″ alternate, even pinnate; leaflets 12 to 38, 1/2″ long, rounded; flowers red, scarlet, orange, showy in dense racemes. Sends out typical pea pods to 5″ long.

NATURE OF TOXICITY

Saponins have been isolated but not chemically defined. Toxins most important in seeds although all plant parts may be toxic. Flowers are also poisonous.

SYMPTOMS

Depression, diarrhea, rapid pulse, weakness, difficult breathing. Symptoms may appear up to two days after ingestion. Deaths have been recorded.

FIRST AID

Seek emergency medical aid. To the paramedic or physician: emesis or gastric lavage may be indicated.

REMARKS

This beautiful plant, considered desirable by many, should not be planted where children might play. Kingsbury suggests removal of bean pods before they open, to prevent poisoning.

Gossypium hirsutum

MOST COMMON NAME: WILD COTTON

WHERE FOUND

Low ridges in wild places. Also planted in many gardens.

COMMON NAME	SCIENTIFIC NAMES
WILD COTTON	*Gossypium hirsutum* *Gossypium barbadense*
	MALVACEAE The MALLOW FAMILY

DESCRIPTION

Small trees or tall shrubs; lobed simple leaves with long petioles. Flower resembles anatomy and general appearance of the familiar Hibiscus; light or white early on, darkening with age to pink. *G. hirsutum* is the species from which the main U.S. cotton crop was developed, although other forms such as *G. barbadense* have contributed to the genetic complex of the cultivated form. Taxonomy is much confused. Seed is covered with long hairs, the familiar cotton fibers of industry.

NATURE OF TOXICITY

Some *Gossypium hirsutum,* depending on the genetic make-up of the plants, contain in their seeds the toxic principle, a pigment called gossypol. It is a polyphenolic compound of little resemblance to other plant products except other related pigments sometimes produced by cotton. Gossypol is located in very tough "glands" visible on seeds—so tough that milling usually does not rupture the glands and the resultant harvest of oil is free of toxicity. Cotton seed cake is rendered almost harmless because the gossypol reacts with other seed parts and becomes inactive. *However,* in the presence of water, the gland walls break down; hence chewing of cotton seed may result in the release of gossypol and its related compounds.

SYMPTOMS

Difficult or labored breathing, gasping, frothing at the mouth. Lungs and kidneys may be congested. More a hazard to livestock; children should, however, be taught to respect this plant.

FIRST AID

Induce vomiting and seek emergency medical aid. Take specimen of offending plant to the physician.

REMARKS

Gossypol, being effective in lowering sperm counts, is being studied in China and the USA as a possible male contraceptive agent.

Melaleuca leucodendron

MOST COMMON NAME: CAJEPUT

WHERE FOUND

Escaped and naturalized in much of South Florida.

COMMON NAMES	SCIENTIFIC NAMES
CAJEPUT Melaleuca Dead Man's Skin Punk Tree	*Melaleuca quinquenervia* (Syn) *M. leucodendron* MYRTACEAE The MYRTLE FAMILY

DESCRIPTION

Large tree to 80′. Bark thick, soft, many-layered, peeling in great patches. Vaguely reminiscent of birch. Leaves alternate, parallel, usually 5-veined, coriaceous, elliptic, green, pointed, short petiole. Leaves 2″–4″ long, aromatic when crushed. Multi-flowered spikes; sepals 1/8″; petals 1/4″ long, white obovate. This form, capable of distributing many thousands of viable seeds from a single fruiting spike, was introduced to Florida by the writer's botany professor of five decades ago, John Gifford. Gifford felt this water-demanding plant would drain the Everglades and convert that "wasteland" into useful farmland. The species today is an out-of-control, top priority weed pest that occupies millions of acres in South Florida. Some forward-thinking communities have outlawed its planting.

NATURE OF TOXICITY

Cajeput oil has long been used as an agent in many old pharmaceutical cough formulae. It contains terpineol and cineole. Taken internally, it is said to relieve gas pain and indigestion. It is employed to cause sweating, and as a stimulant. It can cause gastrointestinal distress and kidney problems in overdose.

SYMPTOMS

Although respiratory problems occur when the plant is in flower, it is not believed to be important as an aeroallergen for the pollen, being sticky, is not airborne. At flowering time, a gaseous allergenic substance may be released. Some authorities claim that asthmatics can have an unpleasant exacerbated respiratory condition due to the presence of nearby flowering *Melaleuca*. Scratches from broken branches, chewed leaves, flowers or seed pods often result in dermal rashes, blisters, and inflammation of epithelia.

FIRST AID

If the problem is skin exposure, wash with Fels-Naptha bar soap and water. If respiratory, remove patient from vicinity of the source tree or from bonfires where *Melaleuca* logs may be employed as firewood. If symptoms are serious, seek emergency medical aid.

Caryota mitis

A. Winterbotham

MOST COMMON NAME: FISHTAIL PALM

WHERE FOUND

Popular garden and patio exotic from Asia.

COMMON NAME	SCIENTIFIC NAMES
FISHTAIL PALM	*Caryota mitis* and *Caryota urens* PALMAE The PALM FAMILY

DESCRIPTION

Spineless, with tall, ringed caudex, *C. mitis* is many-trunked. *C. urens*, with a single trunk, is included here, for both species present similar problems. Leaves delta-shaped, abundant, spirally symmetrical, twice pinnate. Leaf segments are dentate, irregularly split distally. Large green or purple fruit. *C. urens* yields a wine or toddy which is a popular beverage in its native India. Fruits cherry-sized, globular, purple in color.

NATURE OF TOXICITY

The fruit kernel is actually edible, but the surrounding juicy pulp has a very irritating property as yet not identified.

SYMPTOMS

Fruit pulp causes a serious dermatitis that produces swelling and skin lesions which last for a long period. In the eyes, severe irritation and temporary blindness may result.

FIRST AID

Wash skin thoroughly with strong yellow laundry soap such as Fels-Naptha. Flush eyes with copious quantities of water. Seek medical aid.

REMARKS

Probably not a serious threat to children, who immediately feel discomfort on handling fruit or putting it into the mouth, and thus tend to leave it alone.

Phytolacca americana

MOST COMMON NAME: POKEWEED

WHERE FOUND

Oldfields, other disturbed (often filled) land.

COMMON NAMES	SCIENTIFIC NAMES
POKEWEED Pokeberry Scoke Garget	*Phytolacca americana* (Syn) *P. decandra* PHYTOLACCACEAE The POKEWEED FAMILY

DESCRIPTION

Weedy, perennial herbaceous plant growing to 15′; purple or reddish stem may be 2″ in diameter, commonly much smaller. Leaves oval-oblong or oblong-lanceolate, narrowing both directions; acuminate, petiole margined; flowers purplish or greenish-white in peduncled racemes and borne on stout pedicels. Ovary ripens into a flat purple berry. Root stout and cone-shaped.

NATURE OF TOXICITY

Most parts of plant contain GI irritant and CNS toxin. The young shoots are an exception and are commonly eaten as pot greens, although we do not recommend this. (They must be cooked thoroughly in three waters, discarding each to eliminate any toxicity. Also, extreme care *must* be taken *not* to include any root material among the pot greens. IMPROPER PREPARATION HAS CAUSED DEATH!) Toxic agents are saponin, phytolaccine, and phytolaccotoxin.

SYMPTOMS

Violent vomiting, retching, burning of GI tract, cramps, vision impairment, drowsiness, respiratory failure, convulsions, death.

FIRST AID

Induce vomiting. Seek emergency medical aid. Take specimens of plants or vomitus if available.

REMARKS

While accounts of early and present-day rural Americans eating the young shoots are common in our culture, it is suggested that this tasty wild food be left alone unless one is willing to undertake exceptional precautions in its preparation.

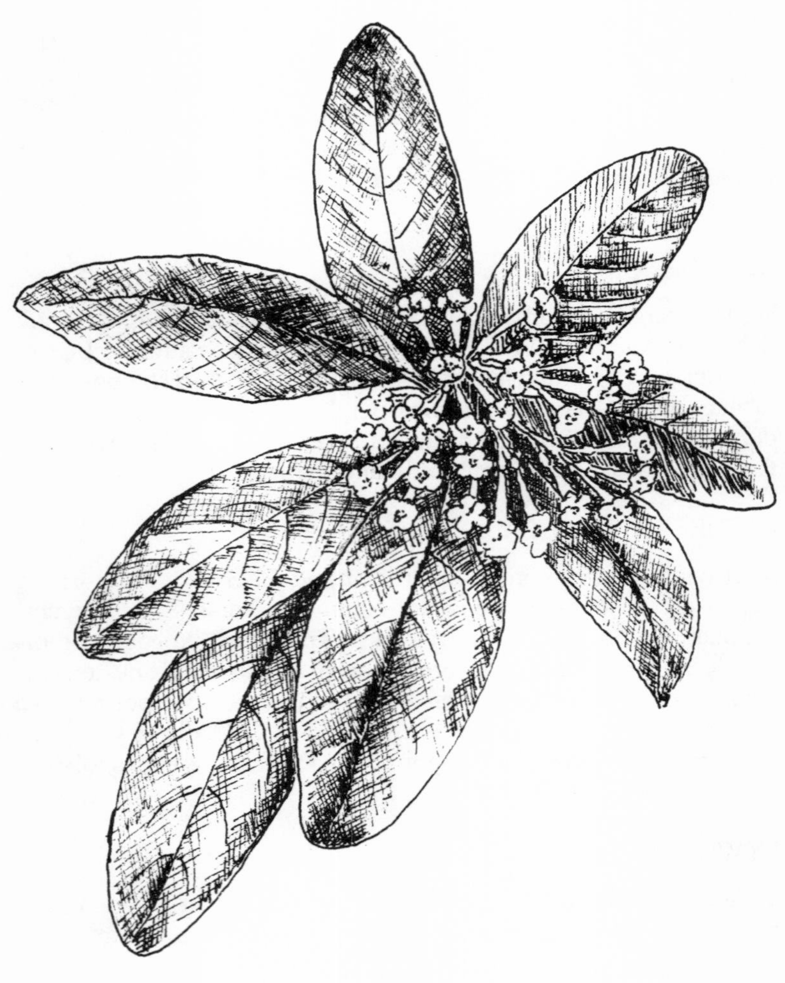

Cestrum diurnum A. Winterbotham

MOST COMMON NAME: DAY JASMINE

WHERE FOUND

Gardens. Also naturalized in many parts of Florida. Native of tropical America.

COMMON NAMES

DAY JASMINE
Day Jessamine

SCIENTIFIC NAME

Cestrum diurnum

SOLANACEAE
The NIGHTSHADE FAMILY

DESCRIPTION

Smooth shrub to 6′; numerous branching stems; entire leaves 2″–4″; coriacious. Flowers white; berry roundish, shiny black, juicy. Pleasant fragrance.

NATURE OF TOXICITY

Fragrance not analyzed. Leaves contain chlorogenic acid, an important allergen. Fruit sap is toxic; agent(s) not identified.

SYMPTOMS

The fragrance, agreeable to many, may cause respiratory depression in others; fear, headache, nausea, vertigo, extreme air passage irritation. Eating fruit may cause gastroenteritis, liver congestion, kidney disease and central nervous system (CNS) damage; tinnitis; vertigo.

FIRST AID

Seek emergency medical aid. Induce emesis. Suggest gastric lavage if problems result from ingestion.

REMARKS

Eradicate from your garden if children are present or visit. In the late 1970's an incident of a child eating *Cestrum* fruit occurred on Sanibel. Jennifer Workman, small daughter of the then director of the Sanibel-Captiva Conservation Foundation sampled this fruit. Fast action averted tragedy, but the case stimulated our first interest in toxic plants, which have been of concern ever since, resulting, finally, in this work.

Cestrum nocturnum

A. Winterbotham

MOST COMMON NAME: NIGHT-BLOOMING JASMINE

WHERE FOUND

Gardens; a common landscape plant.

COMMON NAMES	SCIENTIFIC NAME
NIGHT-BLOOMING JASMINE Night-Blooming Jessamine Poison Berry	*Cestrum nocturnum* SOLANACEAE The NIGHTSHADE FAMILY

DESCRIPTION

Shrubs with branching stems and entire leaves. Inch-long tubular flowers, green-white, with heavy, sickeningly sweet nighttime aroma. Closed and odorless in daytime. Fleshy fruit white, juicy, roundish, oblong. $^1/_2$″.

NATURE OF TOXICITY

Fragrance not analyzed. Leaves contain chlorogenic acid, an important allergen. Fruit sap is toxic, agent(s) not identified.

SYMPTOMS

The overwhelming nocturnal fragrance, agreeable to many, may cause respiratory depression in others; fear, headache, nausea, vertigo, and extreme air passage irritation. Eating fruit may cause gastroenteritis, tachycardia, liver congestion, kidney disease and C.N.S. damage, tinnitis, vertigo, elevated temperature, salivation and paralysis.

FIRST AID

Seek emergency medical aid. Induce emesis; suggest gastric lavage if problems result from ingestion.

REMARKS

Eradicate this plant from your garden, especially if children are present.

Datura candida

A. Winterbottom 8/82

MOST COMMON NAME: ANGEL'S TRUMPET

WHERE FOUND

Gardens.

COMMON NAME	SCIENTIFIC NAME
ANGEL'S TRUMPET	*Datura candida* *Brughansia* is syn. for *Datura* SOLANACEAE The NIGHTSHADE FAMILY

DESCRIPTION

Shrub or small tree, to 14′ tall. Long, softly pubescent leaves 1′ or longer; huge pendulous flowers to 12″, trumpet-shaped, musky sweet scent which, though pleasant to some, is linked with headache, ataxia, and nausea in others.

NATURE OF TOXICITY

All parts (leaves, stem, flowers and seeds) are very toxic—deadly as the Devil! Contains the solanaceous alkaloids scopolamine (now employed as a seasickness remedy), atropine, and hyoscyamine.

SYMPTOMS

Dry, burning mouth; impaired vision; difficulty in swallowing. Hallucination can follow ingestion of parts. Muscular incoordination. Psychogenic. See following species, for all *Datura* spp. exhibit, in their constellation of symptoms, similarities as all have the three cited alkaloids in differing proportions.

FIRST AID

Seek emergency medical aid at once. Collect specimens for positive identification. To paramedic and/or physician: gastric lavage and 1 to 4 mg of I.V. physostigmine salicylate. This drug reverses the acute delirium and reduces temperature within a short time. Do NOT give phenothiazine, a standard drug for the treatment of toxic delirium. Phenothiazine in these cases can cause radically-lowered blood pressure, an alpha block resulting in shock and, often, death.

REMARKS

Has been employed in criminal activities. TEACH YOUR CHILDREN TO LEAVE ALL *DATURA* SPP. UNTOUCHED, including Jimson Weed, *Datura stramonium,* a common plant in North Florida.

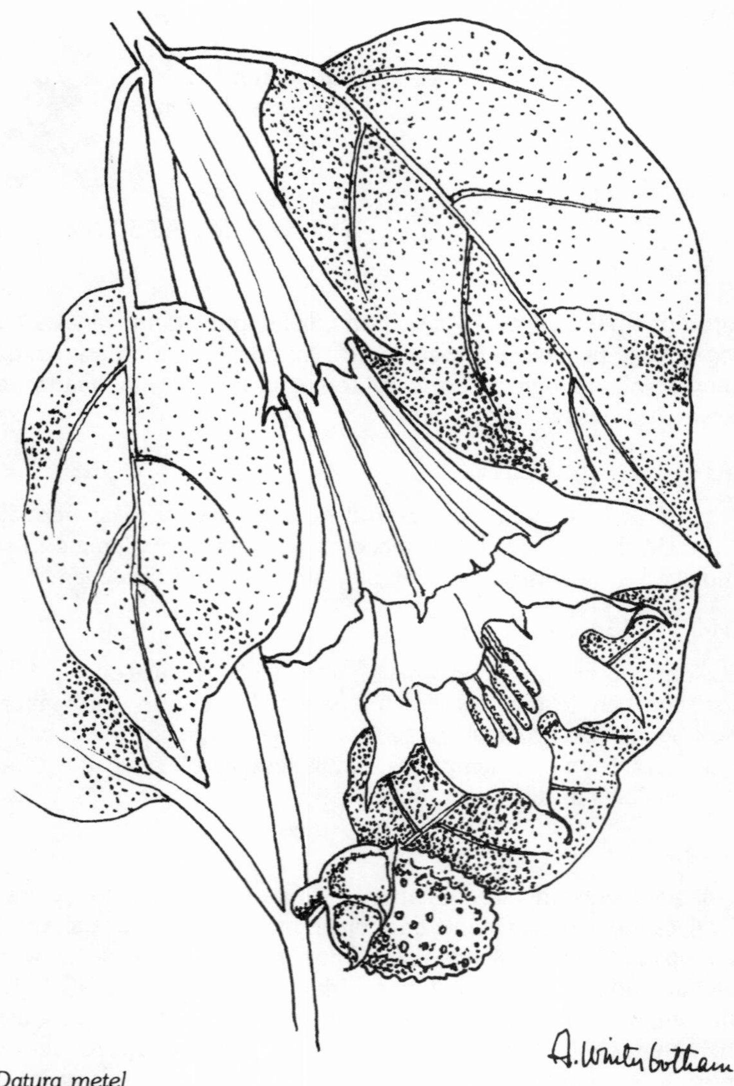

Datura metel

MOST COMMON NAME: DEVIL'S TRUMPET

WHERE FOUND

Popular plant widely grown in Florida gardens.

COMMON NAMES	SCIENTIFIC NAMES
DEVIL'S TRUMPET	*Datura metel*
Hairy Thorn Apple	(Syn) *D. fastuosa*
Downy Thorn Apple	
Criminal's Delight	SOLANACEAE
	The NIGHTSHADE FAMILY

DESCRIPTION

Annual shrub or herb 5′–6′ tall. Leaves pubescent; stems purple and green. Flowers 6″–8″ long, trumpet-shaped corollas. The variety grown in Florida is usually double, reddish-lavender on the outside, light whitish-lavender inside. Seed pod round, 1″, rough, spiny, with many seeds.

NATURE OF TOXICITY

All parts contain atropine, scopolamine, and some hyoscyamine—very toxic. This plant has been widely used in crime.

SYMPTOMS

Dilated and fixed pupils; dry, burning mouth; difficulty in swallowing. Persistent hallucinatory reactions are present: delirium; excitement to drowsiness, muscular incoordination, complete disorientation. Systolic blood pressure ("upper" number) markedly increased; diastolic ("lower" number) markedly decreased.

FIRST AID

Seek emergency medical aid at once. Collect specimens for positive identification. To the paramedic and/or physician: gastric lavage and 1 to 4 mg of I.V. physostigmine salicylate. This drug reverses the acute delirium and reduces temperature within a short time. Do NOT give phenothiazine, a standard drug for the treatment of toxic delirium. Phenothiazine in these cases can cause radically lowered blood pressure, an alpha block resulting in shock and, often, death.

REMARKS

A long history of nefarious uses of this plant's poison properties exists. Seeds have found their way to the street drug trade. To breathe or ingest any part of this plant is extremely dangerous. It has been said that *Datura* provides "a new low in highs"!

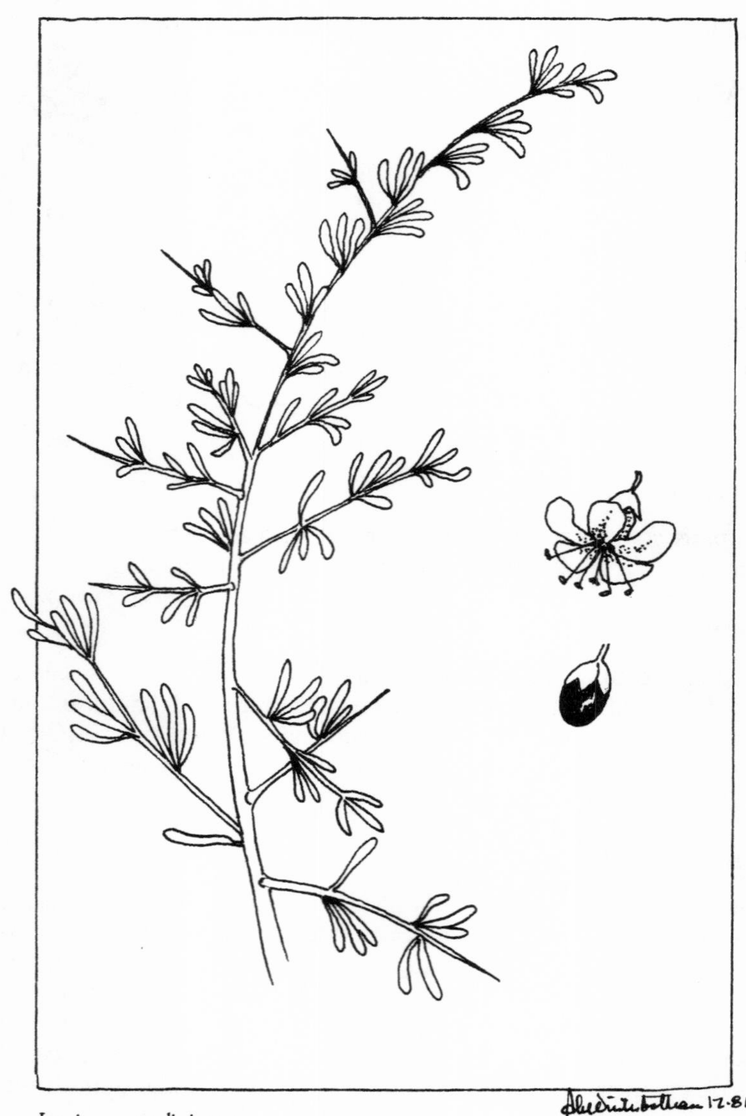

Lycium carolinianum

MOST COMMON NAME: CHRISTMAS BERRY

WHERE FOUND

Common native plant of upland wetlands.

COMMON NAMES	SCIENTIFIC NAME
CHRISTMAS BERRY Matrimony Vine Box Thorn	*Lycium carolinianum* SOLANACEAE The NIGHTSHADE FAMILY

DESCRIPTION

Shrub or small tree to 6′ or 8′ tall. Branches spiny. Leaves thick, dark green, $^1/_4$″ to $^3/_4$″ long, alternate, entire, petiole short. Flowers axillary, solitary, light blue. Fruit red berry.

NATURE OF TOXICITY

Red berries are thought to be toxic; nature of toxicity not established. Botanical position of the genus suggests that the unknown poisonous principle is related to solanaceous alkaloids.

SYMPTOMS

Gastrointestinal distress, excitement, convulsions have been observed in animals. Fatality must be considered a possibility if attractive red berries are consumed.

FIRST AID

Seek emergency medical aid. Induce vomiting. Stomach lavage.

REMARKS

Discourage children from handling the attractive fruit.

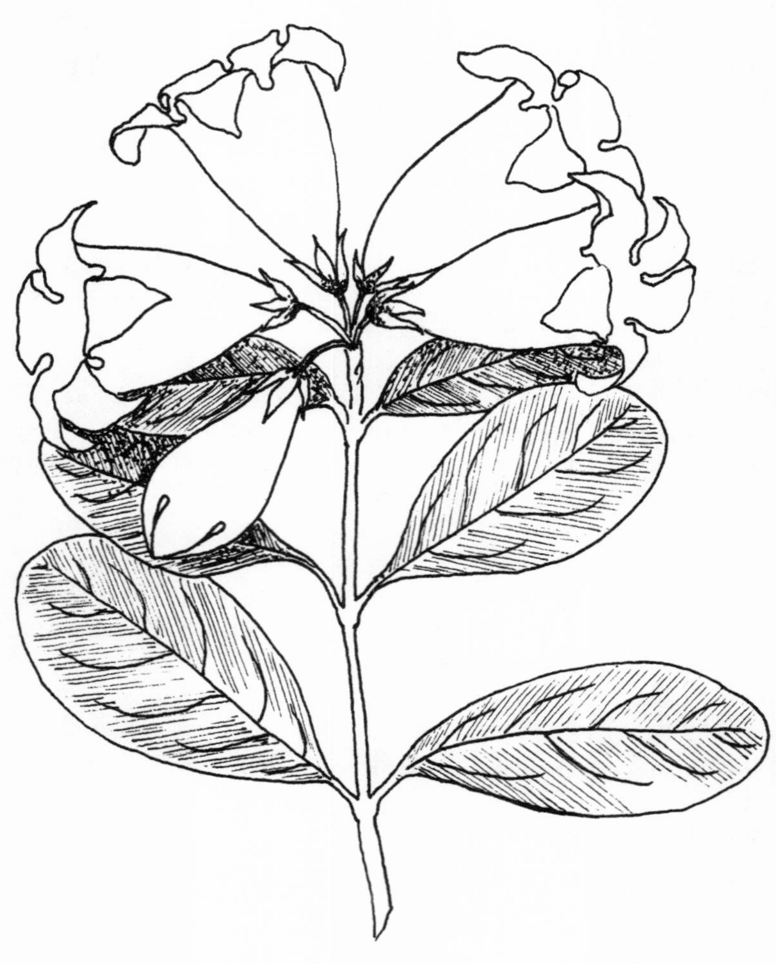

Solandra guttata

MOST COMMON NAME: CHALICE VINE

WHERE FOUND

Gardens.

COMMON NAME

CHALICE VINE
Trumpet Flower

SCIENTIFIC NAME

Solandra guttata

SOLANACEAE
The NIGHTSHADE FAMILY

DESCRIPTION

Long, woody, smooth (glabrous) vines with shiny entire leaves with large showy flowers. Leaves leathery, shiny; flower to 10″, funnelform, yellow or white cylindrical. There are about four *Solandra* species commonly grown here. Native to South America, these attractive plants are much sought after as spectacular garden specimens.

NATURE OF TOXICITY

All parts, especially the flowers, contain the toxic alkaloid solandrine, which by some authors is called solanine.

SYMPTOMS

Solandrine is an hallucinogenic drug, and causes delirium. When eaten, even a small part of a flower can cause death. Other symptoms: dilated pupils, unsteady and irregular muscular movement, unsteady gait, swelling, edema, psychotic symptoms. Flower aroma causes allergenic responses in some people. Sap from stem or leaf a problem in the eye or other epithelial tissues.

FIRST AID

If condition results from topical application to mucosa or eye, flush thoroughly and seek emergency medical aid. In the event of ingestion, seek emergency medical aid and induce vomiting.

REMARKS

It is suggested that *Solandra* spp. not be grown in Florida gardens.

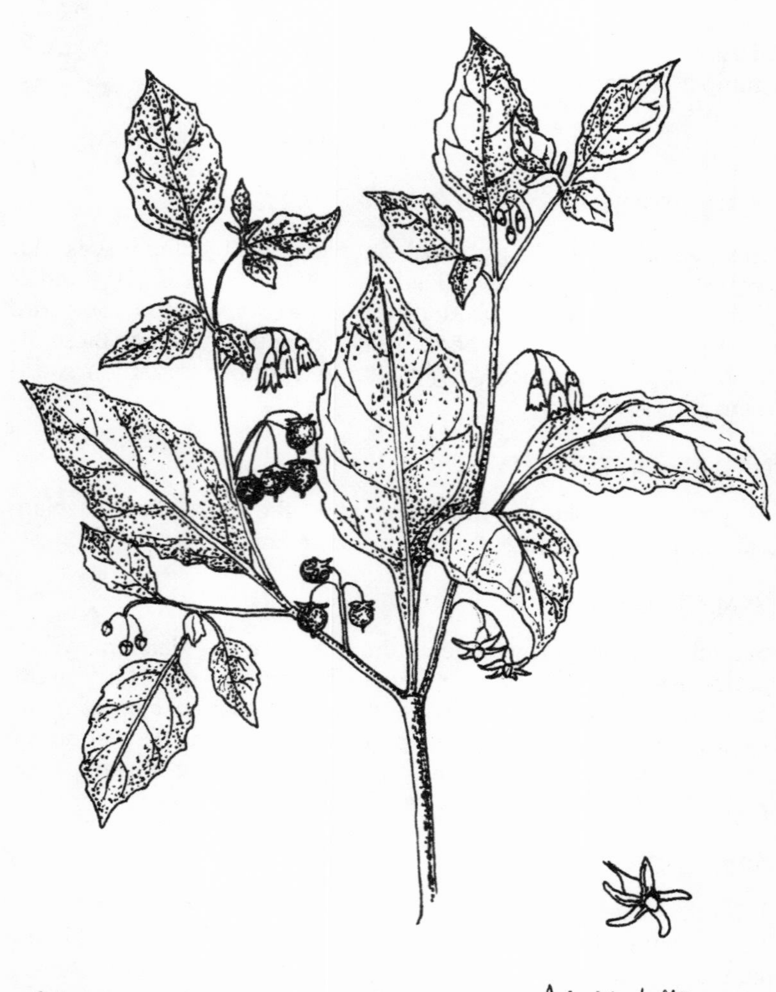

Solanum americanum

MOST COMMON NAME: NIGHTSHADE

WHERE FOUND

In disturbed land, roadsides, vacant lots.

COMMON NAME	SCIENTIFIC NAME
NIGHTSHADE	*Solanum* spp.
	SOLANACEAE The NIGHTSHADE FAMILY

DESCRIPTION

There are some 1500 spp. in worldwide distribution. Some 9 or 10 species occur in South Florida: some native, some exotic introductions. All are under suspicion of being toxic in some degree.

A typical Florida form, *Solanum americanum* is 2′–4′ tall; simple ovate or lanceolate leaves, serrated or entire. Flowers white. Ripe berry is black or dark red. Flowers with 5 sepals, 5 petals, 5 stamens. Hybridization and polyploidy (more than 2 sets of haploid chromosomes) are common phenomena in *Solanum*, making positive identification often impossible.

NATURE OF TOXICITY

For years the name solanine was given to the commonly-recognized toxic alkaloid found in members of genus *Solanum*. Later study showed solanine to be a glycoalkaloid since, when hydrolyzed, it produces a sugar as well as an alkamine. The sugar is called solanose. The alkamine is solanidine. More research has shown there to be many sugars and many alkamines among the many hundreds of *Solanum* species.

SYMPTOMS

Nightshades have been thought to be poisonous plants since ancient times. It is now thought that any given species may be toxic in part of its range and less toxic in others, depending on soil, age, maturity and other variables. Symptoms may be apathy, drowsiness, salivation, dyspnea (difficulty in breathing), trembling, weakness, paralysis, prostration, unconsciousness. GI symptoms may overshadow above nervous effects and include anorexia (appetite loss), nausea, abdominal pain, bloody diarrhea.

Solanum melongena esculentum
Eggplant

Lycopersicon esculentum
Tomato

FIRST AID

Seek emergency medical aid. Save specimens of plant and vomitus if any.

REMARKS

It is well to be able to recognize "nightshade" in a general way for it is quite impossible to identify exactly what species is involved, it being such a complex genus. Not all *Solanum* spp. are without value; consider *S. tuberosum,* the Potato. As a matter of fact, three solanceous plants are of great value in the vegetable garden. The eggplant and potato are the genus *Solanum.* The tomato is of a closely allied genus, *Lycopersicon.*

Solanum tuberosum
Potato

Although of great importance in human history, especially during the industrial revolution in Great Britain, the potato can be deadly. Solanine, a glyco-alkaloid, found throughout the plant, is dangerous if the potato is green, spoiled or sprouted.

Lantana camara A. Winterbotham

MOST COMMON NAME: LANTANA

WHERE FOUND

In gardens and disturbed areas.

COMMON NAMES	SCIENTIFIC NAME
LANTANA Shrub Verbena	*Lantana camara* VERBENACEAE The VERBENA FAMILY

DESCRIPTION

Lantana camara has small, showy flowers, yellow, orange and red, in flat clusters, 1″ in diameter. Some varieties yellow, white, buff and lavender. Fruits turning to blue or purple when fully ripe. Stems with prickles. Here *Lantana camara,* an exotic apparently introduced from South America, grows to 10′, but usually 2′–3′. The leaves are aromatic and 1″ to 4″ long, ovate acute acuminate (pointed apex), crenate or dentate (scalloped or toothed edges); rugose above, with articulated veins, rough surface, hispid or hairy.

Lantana ovatifolia is similar, also with showy flowers and toxicity like *L. camara.* Other *Lantana spp.* also present in Florida.

NATURE OF TOXICITY

Unripe fruit, fleshy drupe, very toxic, containing lantanine, a poison. When ripe, blue or purple fruits are eaten by some people. Lantanine is metabolyzed in the liver where phylloerythrin is produced, causing photosensitivity. (Hepatogenic photosensitizer)

SYMPTOMS

Vomiting, diarrhea, weakness, difficulty in breathing, coma, death. Phylloerythrin, the metabolite of lantanine, travels from the liver via the bloodstream to areas free of hair; jaundice may result; yellowing of epithelia, skin lesions, kidney disease, sometimes death. Touching the leaves causes dermatitis.

FIRST AID

Seek emergency medical aid. Induce vomiting if necessary. If skin contact, wash with Fels-Naptha bar soap.

REMARKS

Eradicate from gardens and areas where children play. Even though *Lantana* fruits are thought by some to be edible when fully ripe (blue or purple), we advise *against* eating them, for they are, without doubt, poisonous when unripe (green).

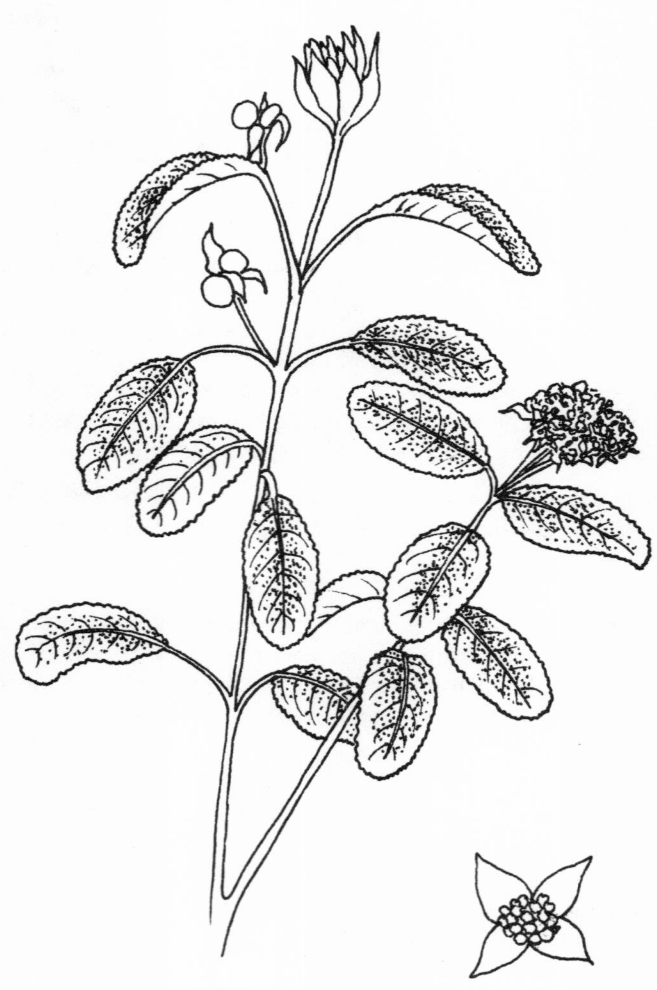

Lantana involucrata

MOST COMMON NAME: WILD LANTANA

WHERE FOUND

Common native plant found in hammocks and scrub areas.

COMMON NAME	SCIENTIFIC NAME
WILD LANTANA	*Lantana involucrata*
	VERBENACEAE The VERBENA FAMILY

DESCRIPTION

Many-branched shrub to 6′ tall. Stems lack spines or prickles. Leaves oval or elliptical, serrate or with rounded teeth; apex obtuse, pubescent above and below. Flower heads $^{1}/_{3}$″ to $1^{1}/_{2}$″, white or pale blue-white. Fruit, when ripe, purple or blue. Edible when completely ripe. Poisonous when unripe.

NATURE OF TOXICITY

Unripe fruit, fleshy drupe, very toxic, containing lantanine, a poison. When ripe, blue or purple fruits are eaten by some people. Lantanine is metabolyzed in the liver where phylloerythrin is produced, causing photosensitivity. (Hepatogenic photosensitizer)

SYMPTOMS

Vomiting, diarrhea, weakness, difficulty in breathing, coma, death. Phylloerythrin, the metabolite of lantanine, travels from the liver via the bloodstream to areas free of hair; jaundice may result, yellowing of epithelia, skin lesions, kidney disease, sometimes death. Touching the leaves causes dermatitis.

FIRST AID

Seek emergency medical aid. Induce vomiting. If contact, wash with Fels-Naptha bar soap.

REMARKS

Considered to be a desirable native plant. Children should be taught to leave it alone.

SECTION II
TOXIC AND VENOMOUS ANIMALS

INTRODUCTION

Among the venomous animals of Florida there are both invertebrates and vertebrates. Some marine and some terrestrial. Not all species will be discussed, but representative forms of major groups will be included.

As in the case of problems with plants, the successful treatment of poisoning or envenomation by animals is best served by the *collection of a specimen* or even a photograph of the offending creature. It's a lot easier and safer, for example, to photograph a big rattlesnake than it is to catch him, or even kill him, for a freshly-beheaded rattlesnake is still capable of biting because muscular reflexes are active for a surprisingly long time. A major problem with the large number of serious spider bites which have occurred in recent years is the fact that people seldom collect good specimens of the offending creatures.

The animals are arranged with the invertebrates first and the vertebrates last.

INVERTEBRATE ANIMALS

PHYLUM PROTOZOA SINGLE-CELLED ANIMALS

RED TIDE

Each year Florida is afflicted by one or more outbreaks of Red Tide—an overabundance of small single-celled flecks of living tissue claimed by both botanists and zoologists. We won't dwell on that argument and will simply call dinoflagellates, as they are named, animals—protozoans. Some dinoflagellates *do* have chlorophyll, so botanists do have a point.

The Red Tide organism of these parts is *Gymnodinium* (also known as *Ptychodiscus*) *brevis* which, when it "over-blooms" increases from its more or less normal 1000 per quart of sea water to literally millions per quart, staining the sea reddish. Hence the name Red Tide.

With each dividing animalcule, toxin is released into the water: Brevitoxin B, named after the animal's specific name, *brevis*. Almost thirty years ago, following the great Red Tide of 1953, scientists at Texas A&M, Cornell, and Columbia Universities joined in an effort to identify the toxin. The common Zebra Fish, *Danio,* of the home aquarium world was the animal model used to test the various toxic "soups" that were derived from artificially-reared *Gymnodinium* at the Texas A&M Galveston facility. This substance, Brevitoxic B, has caused massive fish kills, mollusk poisoning and human food poisoning. Possibly, too, the filter-feeding primitive cordates known as tunicates are part of the chain causing deaths of the manatee, for it is believed that Brevitoxin B concentrates in tunicates which, under certain rare conditions, are inadvertently fed upon by manatees grazing on sea grasses.

Aside from fish kills—sometimes a hundred pounds of dead fish per foot of beach, and correspondingly high costs to the fishing industry (1971 Southwest Florida cost was an estimated $20 million)—people are affected as well. One should not eat filter-feeding mollusks during a *Gymnodinium* outbreak, for concentrations of Brevitoxin B are deposited in the animals and can cause serious illness to people who eat oysters, clams and the like. It is well to pay careful attention to the shellfish bans whenever they are posted.

When a Red Tide is about, one can usually check it out quite easily: facing the onshore breeze, breathe through the mouth. Airborne Brevitoxin B will be felt as a definite throat irritant if present in appreciable concentrations.

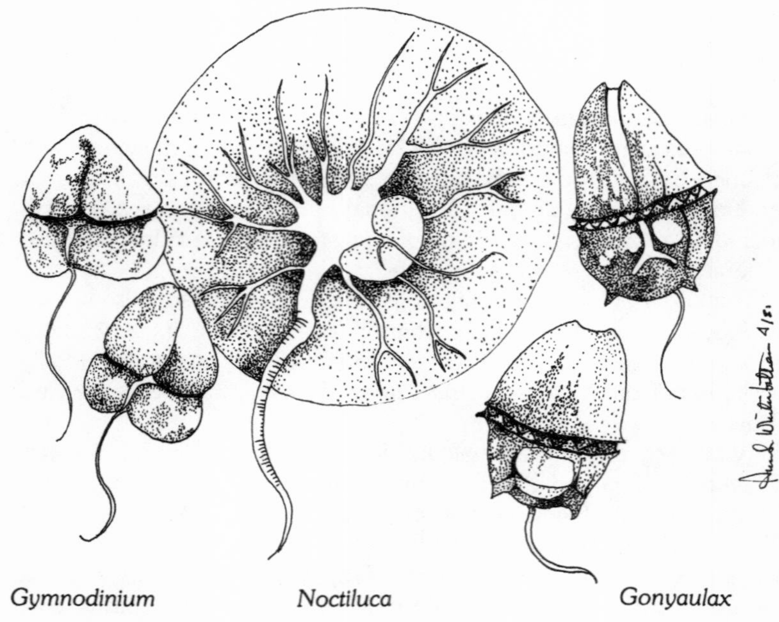

Gymnodinium *Noctiluca* *Gonyaulax*

Pictured here are three dinoflagellates: *Gymnodinium* on the left; *Noctiluca* in the center—a harmless bioluminescent form which sparkles in the water at night and is often present in great numbers in Florida; *Gonyaulax* on the right—a form which causes Red Tide in other oceans.

Efforts to control this natural phenomenon should, perhaps, not be undertaken, costly though Red Tide may be. It must be remembered that most of the earth's oxygen is generated by the marine phytoplankton of the top few feet of ocean water—generated by photosynthesis. Red Tide organisms are part of that planktonic biosystem. Agents employed to kill, say, *Gymnodinium* (*Gomphos-*

pheria has been proposed) might seriously affect the planktonic ecosytem which is basic to life on earth. *Gymnodinium* blooms are natural phenomena as are other Red Tide blooms of other organisms in other oceans. This writer feels that efforts by man to control are ill-advised. When man monkeys with natural phenomena, disaster is usually the harvest.

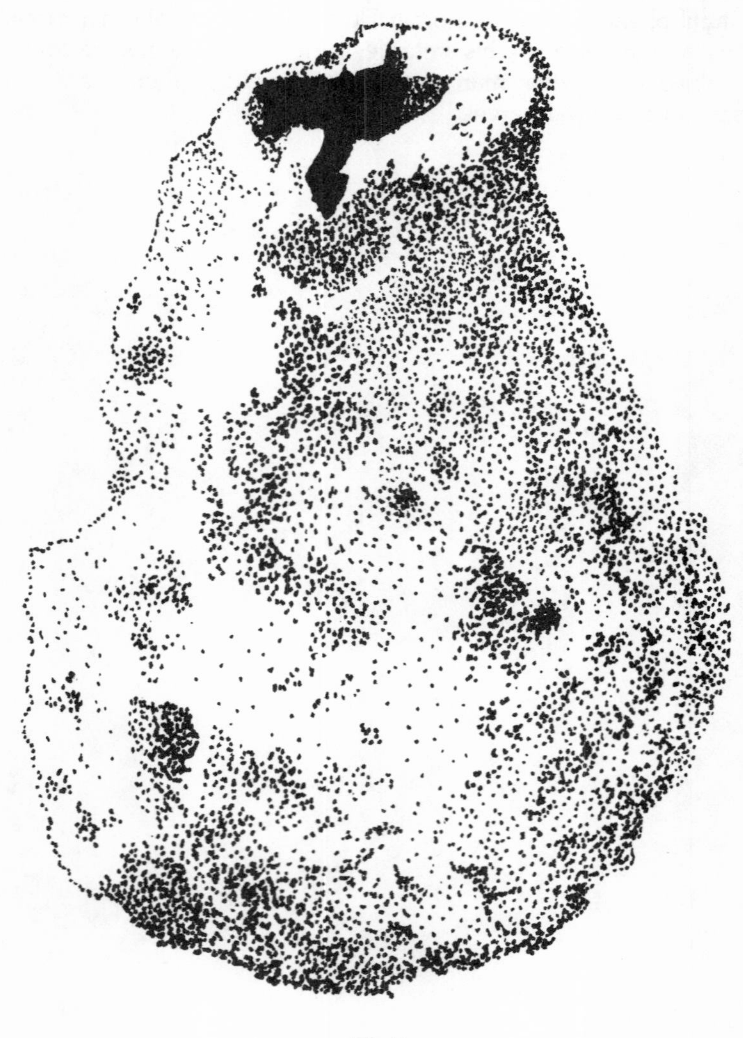

Fibulia

A. Winterbotham

PHYLUM PORIFERA

SPONGES

Sponges are many-celled simple animals found attached to shells, rocks, sometimes pilings. The skeleton we call "sponge" is in some species calcareous (calcium-based). In others, it is siliceous (silicon-based).

The integument is perforated by pores (hence Porifera) through which seawater circulates. The sponge filters out planktonic micro-organisms on which it feeds.

Most sponges are harmless, but occasionally one may find a stinging form. In Florida waters may be found *Fibulia*, the Do-Not-Touch-Me Sponge, and *Tedania*, the Fire Sponge, a bright orange form that can sting and can also cause severe rash.

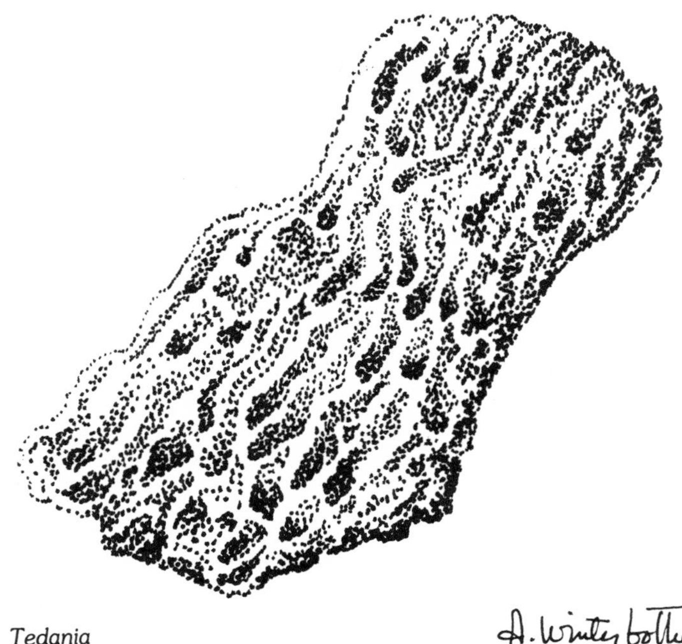

Tedania

A. Winterbotham

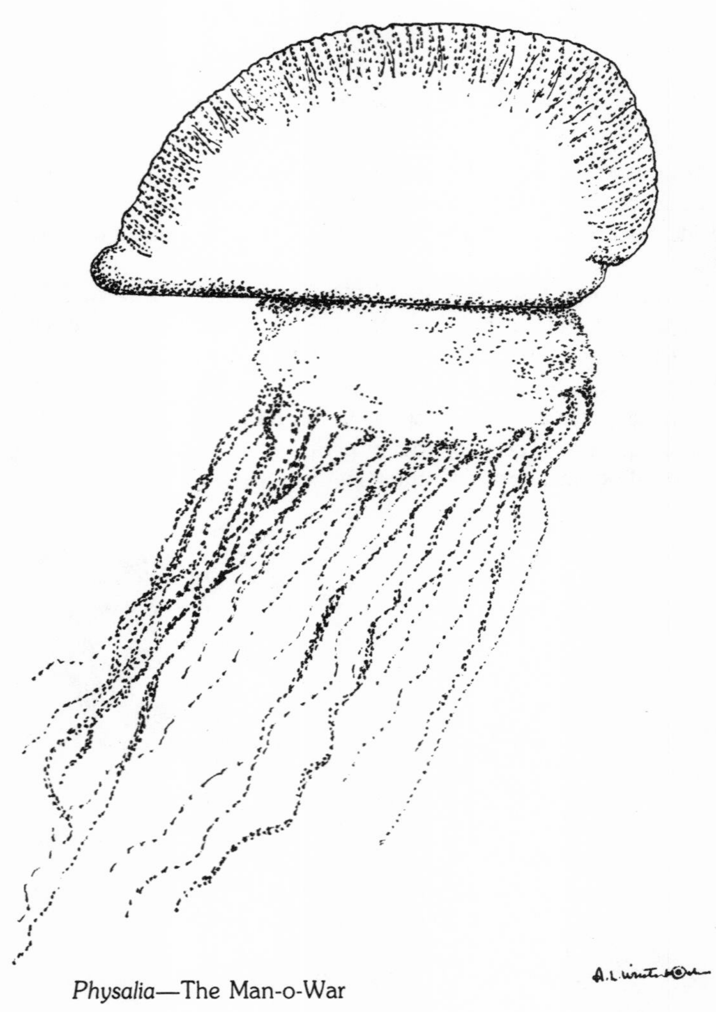

Physalia—The Man-o-War

PHYLUM COELENTERATA

JELLYFISH, CORALS, SEA ANEMONES, HYDROIDS

The Coelenterates may be fixed, like the corals, or pelagic as are jellyfish. Some are colonial, as the corals and the Man-o-War. The latter is common and dangerous on the East Coast of Florida. In general, Coelenterates are radially symmetrical. The Man-o-War, *Physalia* is an exception as each colony is made up of separate specialized individual animals—one to provide flotation, one to provide food, others for digestion, reproduction, etc.

Each Coelenterate has an internal cavity. Alternation of generations occurs—often a sexless fixed generation and a sexual motile or pelagic generation; e.g., the fixed sexless corals have a planktonic sexual stage.

All Coelenterates have a peculiarly effective weapons structure, the nematocyst (see drawing). The nematocyst at rest and cocked, ready to shoot, has coiled within its capsule a sharp, sometimes barbed, poison delivery instrument known as the thread tube. When the "nettle cell" is "fixed" following cnidocil (trigger) contact with potential prey (or you!) the thread tube suddenly straightens out from its coiled position extending out through the operculum or "door" at the end of the capsule for a distance of about two times the length of the resting nematocyst. It is this thread tube that carries the venom—often a paralytic toxin.

All nematocysts on all Coelenterates are venom organs, but only a few are troublesome. Not so in Australasia where there is a lethal killer that can cause instant death. Not so, too, in Dade, Palm Beach (where I was raised, and where I experienced many Man-o-War incidents) and Broward Counties and elsewhere on Florida's east coast, where *Physalia* is often very abundant. These floating colonies may drag 35 foot (or longer) tentacles—hundreds of them, each armed with hundreds of nematocysts. The Man-o-War can cause serious injury. It is not often seen on the west coast due, I believe, to the predominantly north-south clockwise Gulf currents. In ten years I have found only one.

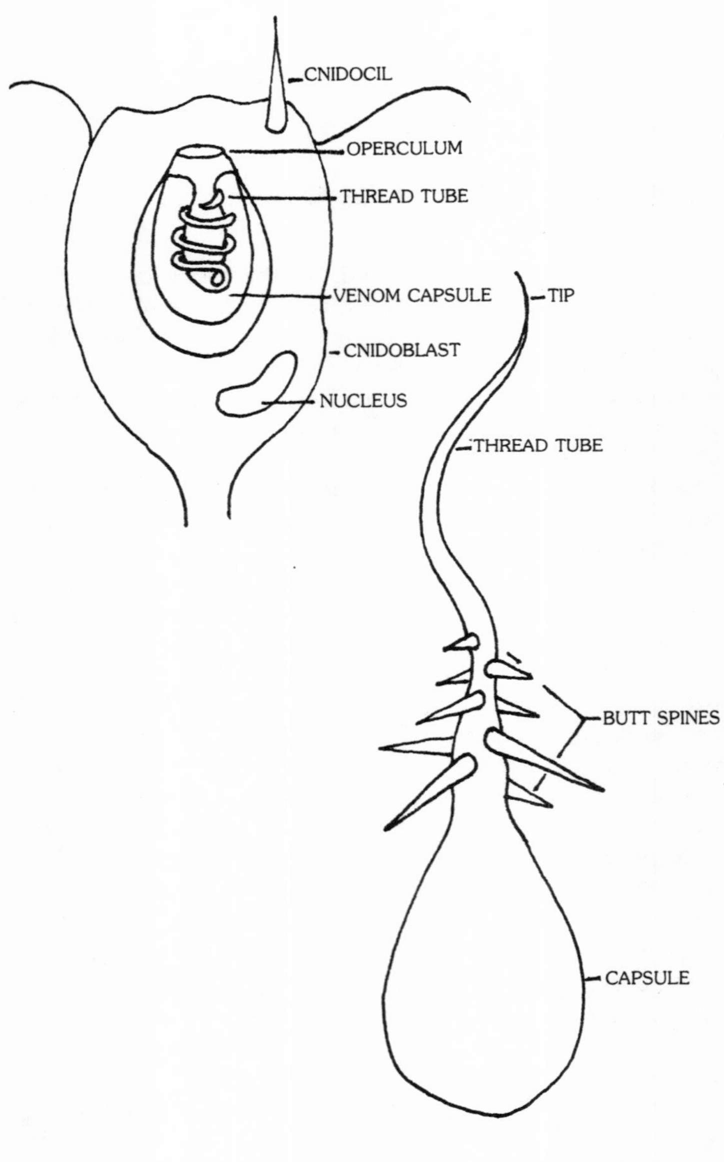
CNIDOCIL
OPERCULUM
THREAD TUBE
VENOM CAPSULE
CNIDOBLAST
NUCLEUS
TIP
THREAD TUBE
BUTT SPINES
CAPSULE
A. Winterbotham

Nematocyst

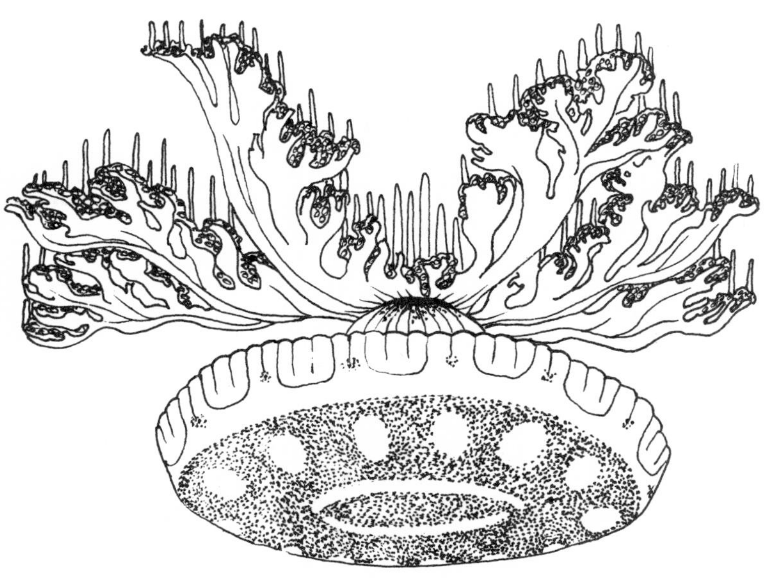

Cassiopeia xamachana A. Winterbotham

Although nematocysts are strictly Coelenterate evolutionary "inventions," other non-Coelenterate groups of animals use them. Sea Slugs eat tentacles of hydroids and do not digest the nematocysts which migrate to the waving back fringes of these mollusks and provide protection. In another instance, an octopus gathers the nematocyst-armed tentacles of the Man-o-War and uses them for defense. Some Sea Cucumbers similarly employ nematocysts of Coelenterate origin.

It is little short of miraculous, to me at least, that animals as unrelated as Coelenterates and mollusks could provide living cells from one to the other for their use! The same comment applies to the Sea Cucumber.

There are many nematocyst structures, but all are modifications of the generalized more or less characteristic one here illustrated. Most are mounted on tentacles.

We have a number of Jellyfishes that can harm you. We suggest you leave all of them untouched. A notable species is pictured here, *Cassiopeia xamachana,* often called the Upside-down Jellyfish. It can be found in still waters, sometimes upside down and sometimes not. It is considered to be in the moderate-to-severe category of danger to man.

Cassiopeia is about 12 or 14 inches in diameter, yellow or brown, often lying on its "back" in shallow water. Stings from this animal may result in skin welts, skin rash, itching, vomiting and skeletal pains.

There is another Jellyfish that ranges into Florida waters, the Giant Jellyfish, *Cyanea capillata,* the very largest of all Coelenterates. It is worthy of mention for no other reason than its enormous size. The bell or "body" can be ten feet in diameter! It trails hundreds of tentacles containing thousands of trigger-happy nematocysts. Tentacles can be over 100 feet long! This form is considered to be an important species because of its capability of inflicting a severe sting.

Stinging or Fire Corals can be found in Florida waters. These pertain to genus *Millepora.* Brushing against a live colony may cause severe pain due to the firing of the minute nematocysts.

SYMPTOMS AND FIRST AID TREATMENT OF COELENTERATE STINGS

If one is stung by Coelenterates, papular eruptions will result, usually in lines (following the incidental patterns of the tentacles). Pain may be severe. Local application of ammonia or vinegar is advocated by some. Meat tenderizer, boric acid, lime juice, petroleum products, dry sand have all been advocated.

Today the preferred first aid is as follows:

1. Wash in sea water.
2. If possible, remove tentacles.
3. Apply alcohol (gin or vodka will do).
4. Pour dry flour, baking soda or apply mentholated shaving soap.
5. Scrape the caked material with a knife.
6. Reapply.
7. Rescrape.

If serious, seek emergency medical aid.

Fire Coral. *Millepora* sp.

Astrophyton sp.

Diadema antillarum
The Black or Needle Spined Sea Urchin

PHYLUM ECHINODERMATA

SEA STARS, BRITTLE STARS, SEA URCHINS, SEA CUCUMBERS

Echino = hedgehog; derm = skin. Therefore Echinodermata = prickly-skinned, radially symmetrical forms, easily recognizable by all seashore visitors.

Of many poisonous forms throughout the world, there are only two hereabouts that are in any way a problem:

1. The most complex of the Brittle Stars, the Basket Star, *Astrophyton* sp. may be poisonous. The literature is silent on how or under what conditions.
2. The Black Sea Urchin or Needle Spined Urchin, *Diadema antillarum,* is a risky organism. In clear, deep waters it is found in passes, on bridge supports, reefs and rocks. It is a menace to divers. The long-barbed spines easily enter the flesh and readily break off. Festering, stinging wounds of long duration result, it being very difficult to remove all of the spine fragments.

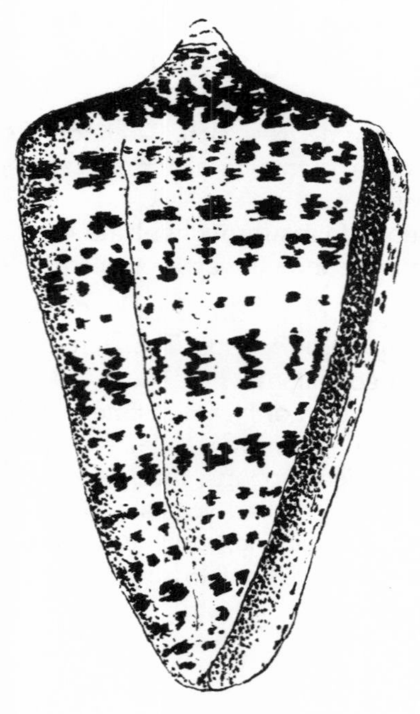

A more or less typical looking cone shell of the genus *Conus*

PHYLLUM MOLLUSCA

SNAILS, BIVALVES, OCTOPI, SQUID, etc.

One of Florida's greatest natural treasures is the molluscan fauna for which we are known throughout the world. Few, if any, of our species are dangerously venomous.

Cones of the genus *Conus* may be dangerous, for all members of this genus are generally considered to be venomous. For example, *Conus gloriamaris,* a rare Indo-Pacific form, can kill with its venom apparatus. Most of the literature states that Florida cones are harmless, or almost harmless. However Halstead lists them with the rest and calls them "venomous." It is possible that some allergic or sensitive people could be envenomated by these species, so it is well to use care in handling live specimens.

Three cones of this region are the Alphabet Cone, *Conus spurius atlanticus;* Florida Cone, *C. floridanus;* Crown Cone, *C. regius.* Some authors list up to a dozen more species from Florida. The possible dangerous nature of these animals may induce potential collectors to leave them alone.

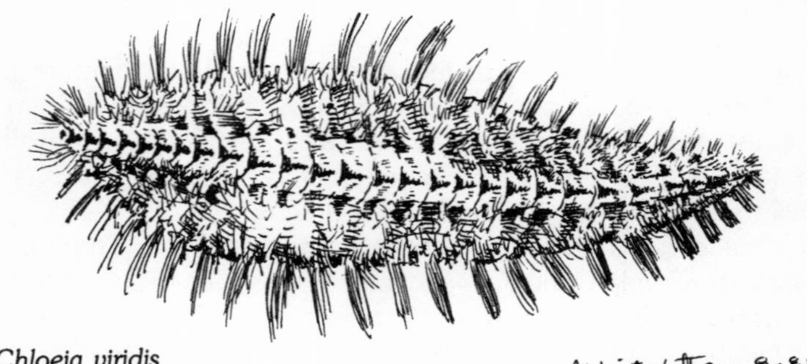

Chloeia viridis

A. Winterbottom 8-82

PHYLUM ANNELIDA

THE SEGMENTED WORMS

The most widely-known Annelids are the common earthworms which are known to all. Many Annelids have bristles—even earthworms—but in our marine environment there are three Polychaete Bristle Worm species, all pertaining to family Amphinomidae. All have tufts of lateral bristles, two tufts to each segment. One species grows to about one foot—the Green Bristle Worm, *Hermodice carunculata.* It has a square body, green general color and white bristles. When handled, the bristles penetrate the skin and cause excruciating pain of long duration. Two others, somewhat smaller, are *Eurythoe complanata,* the Orange Bristle Worm, attaining six inches, and *Chloeia viridis* (pictured), the Red-tipped Bristle Worm. The latter is smaller, much more bristly. The bristles of both species can cause pain. *Handle with care*—or better yet, do not touch!

SYMPTOMS

Painful stings from bristles.

FIRST AID

Follow general comments under Coelenterates. Attempt to remove embedded spines or fragments. Seek emergency medical aid if there is a serious condition.

PHYLUM ARTHROPODA

ARTHROPODS

Segmented invertebrate animals with jointed legs and a thickened chitinous cuticle forming an exoskeleton:

CLASS INSECTA, INSECTS

CLASS ARACHNIDA, ARACHNIDS

CLASS INSECTA
ORDER HYMENOPTERA

ANTS, BEES, WASPS, HORNETS, YELLOW JACKETS

Hymenoptera have two pairs of wings—the two on each side are hooked together with a "hymen." This seldom is clearly shown in illustrations. Of course most ants don't have wings, except when young winged ones fly out into the world on the nuptial excursion seeking new nest sites.

ANTS

There are many ant species in Florida including the Native and Imported (Brazilian) Fire Ants of the genus *Solenopsis*. The latter was first brought to Alabama early in the century presumably via a cargo vessel from Brazil. It is sometimes $^1/_4$" long or more and builds low conical mounds two to three feet in diameter. It can deliver a painful bite that may fester and blister, but it is not worthy of the panicky chemical warfare that has taken place in the southeastern U.S. for the last several decades. Our native, much smaller, Fire Ants can also deliver painful bites.

Fire Ants are easy to avoid if you are observant. Most bites occur when one carelessly, without thought, stands on or near a colony. When finally noticed, dozens or even hundreds of fire ants can be swarming up your legs and over your body.

Better and safer than noxious chemicals, a kettle of boiling water will often destroy a colony.

BEES, WASPS, HORNETS AND YELLOW JACKETS

These may be collectively considered. At certain times of the year, as when Brazilian Pepper is in flower or when Mangroves or oranges bloom, professional apiculturists move hundreds of hives of honey bees to exploit such areas.

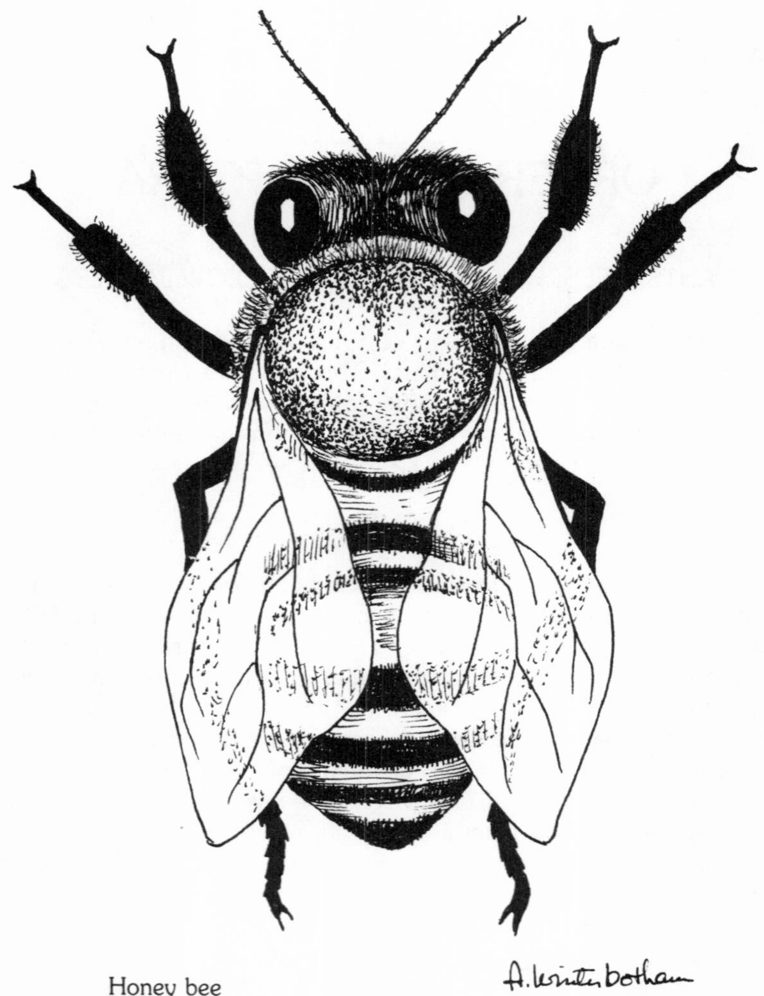

Honey bee

Gigantic Yellow Jacket colonies have been observed and hornets and wasps are abundant in Florida.

Some people are allergic to insect venoms and should take special precautions as follows:

a. Avoid scented hair preparations, perfumes and the like, for they can be attractive to the insects.
b. Carry in your purse or glove compartment an aerosol spray can of some harmless (i.e., non-toxic to humans) insecticide.

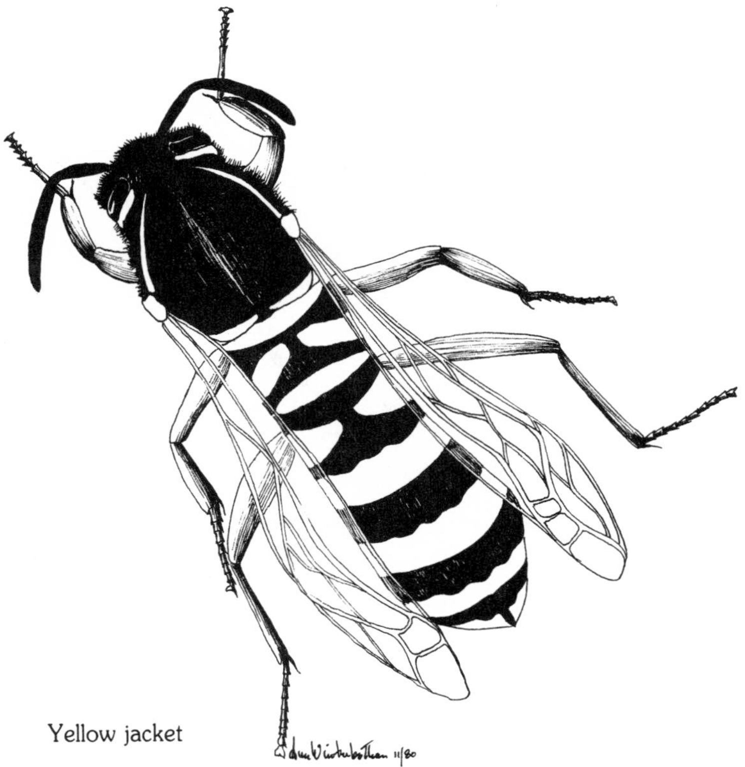

Yellow jacket

A spray that is largely pyrethrum-based should do. Such safe sprays can be found in pet shops.

c. For some, it is advisable to carry an emergency kit containing aerosol Adrenalin as well as an oral antihistimine. For those in danger of anaphylactic shock, the family doctor can prescribe a kit. Such people should keep this kit at hand at all times.

FIRST AID

If stinger is left in the wound (as in bee stings) remove it *without squeezing it.* Scrape it out with a knife point.

Apply ice—it slows down absorption of the venom and its chemical activity.

Seek emergency medical aid if any of the following symptoms are present: shortness of breath, swelling, wheezing, abdominal pain, cramps, fainting, shock.

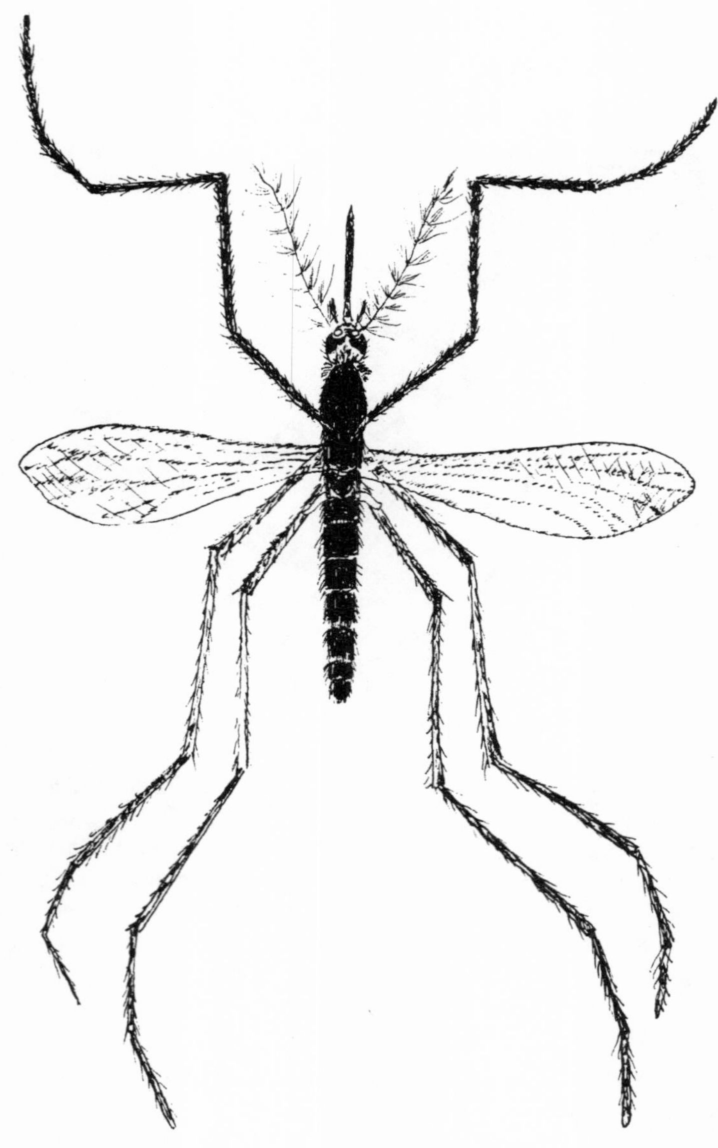

Culex nigripalpus vectors St. Louis Encephalitis (SLE)

CLASS INSECTA
ORDER DIPTERA

FLIES AND MOSQUITOES

There are more than five dozen mosquito species in Florida! Most are harmless nuisance mosquitoes; some do vector disease. For example, *Culex nigripalpus*, a very localized short-flighted fresh-water form has been implicated in the occurrence of St. Louis Encephalitis (SLE). Sentinel chickens are employed to check for SLE.

Anopheles spp., of which there are more than a dozen, could vector malaria if there were a reservoir of malaria plasmodia present. No such reservoir has existed in Florida in recent times. The principal nuisance mosquitoes are *Aedes taeniorhynchus*, and other Salt Marsh species. *A. taeniorhynchus* does not vector disease in Florida though the species has been implicated in Dengue elsewhere in its range. This form exists in huge abundance and has adapted to the environmental insults perpetrated by Mosquito Control Districts, for there are days when it swarms in countless millions, much to the torment of unadaptable people.

Far better than to kill the birds and the bees—and dragonflies which naturally FEED on mosquitoes—by massive applications of lethal organophosphate poisons, is to create your own micro-habitat which is unattractive to mosquitoes. I refer to the application of insect repellent—by far the best of which is Muskol brand.

Aedes taeniorhynchus can fly 25 miles. So the ones biting you today may have originated far away.

The organophosphates represent a fall-out from the nerve gas technology of WWII. German research under Hitler developed these substances which depress cholinesterases, substances very important in normal nerve impulse transmission.

Other flies of importance here are the No-See-Ums or Sand Flies of the Genus *Culicoides*. Pictured here is *C. furens*, the Furious Sand Fly. Personal micro-habitat alteration is the best treatment, for Mosquito Control Districts do not have No-See-Um-programs.

House flies, *Musca domestica*, although not really poisonous, are

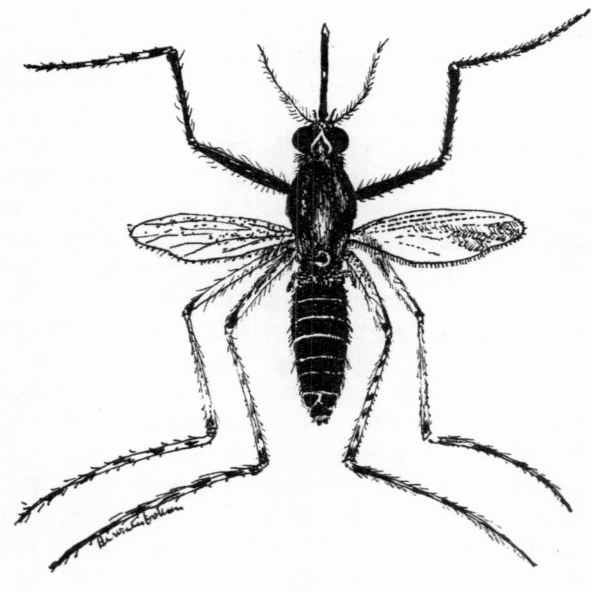

Aedes taeniorhynchus

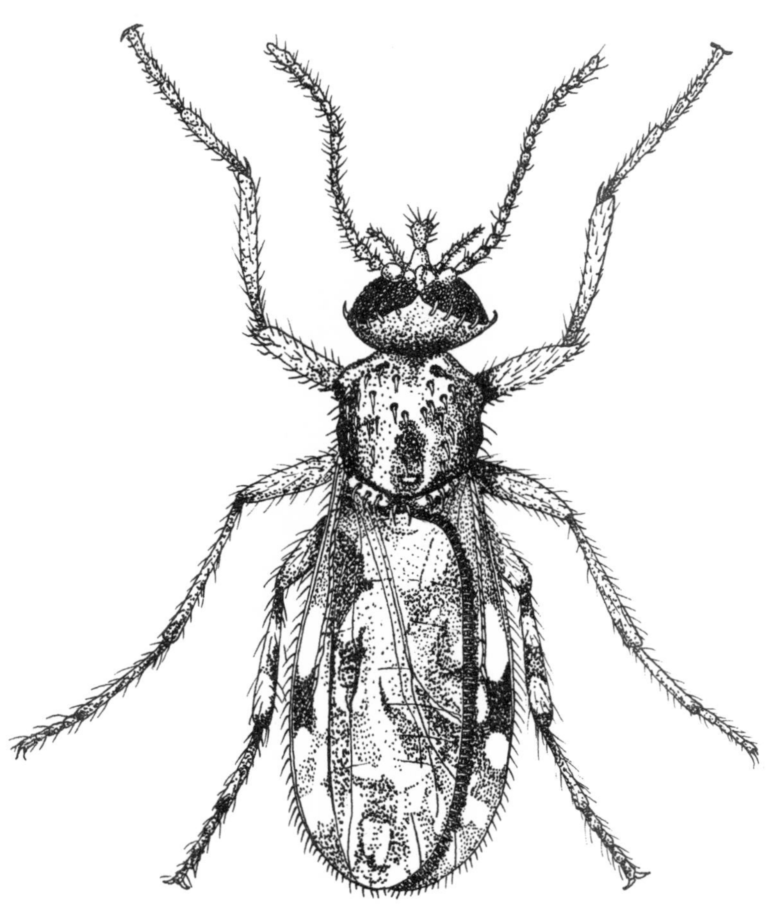

Culicoides furens
The Furious Sand Fly—one of the No-See-Um forms. In life it is smaller than a period.

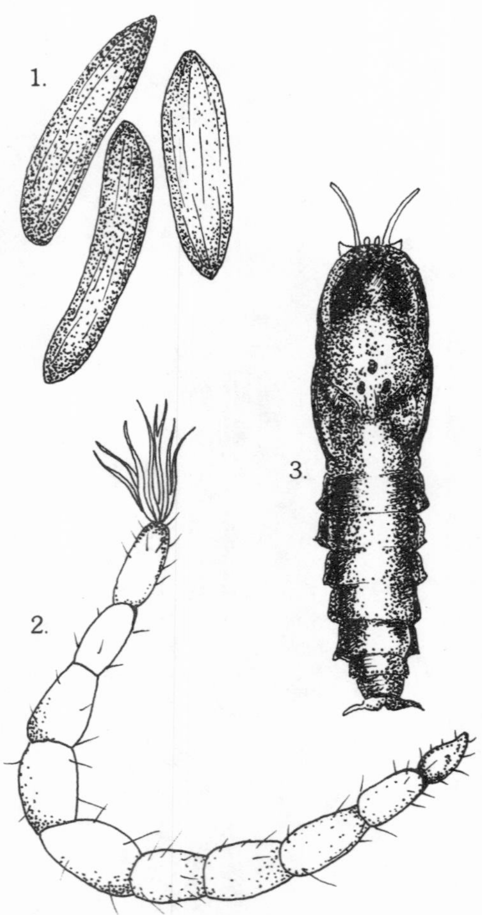

1. Eggs 2. Larva 3. Pupa
of *Culicoides* sp.

regarded as a great threat to human health because they transmit a large number of important diseases—typhoid, cholera, dysentery and various parasites. Present also are biting flies of the family *Tabanidae* (the Deer flies, *Chrysops spp.* and Horseflies, *Tabanus spp.*). Biting Stable Flies, *Stomoxys calcitrans,* occur in Florida as do a number of other flies that cause painful lesions.

CLASS ARACHNIDA
ARACHNIDS

SPIDERS, TICKS, SCORPIONS, MITES, CHIGGERS

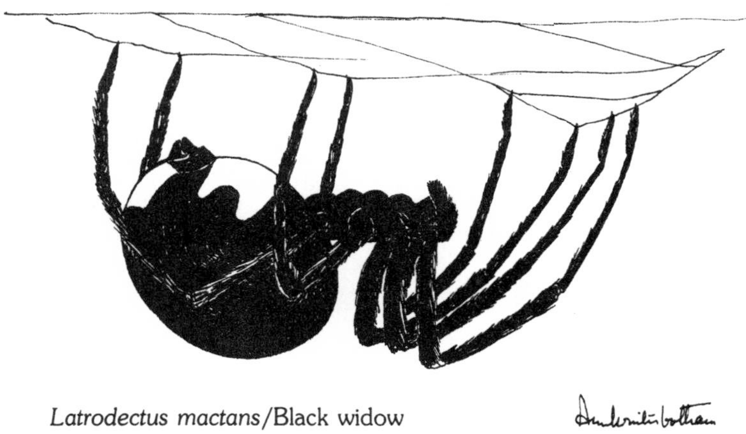

Latrodectus mactans/Black widow

SPIDERS

All spiders are venomous. However most forms are harmless because of the small size of the biting mouth parts and low toxicity of many spider venoms.

Black Widow Spiders, *Latrodectus mactans* are very common throughout much of Florida. The Red Widow Spider, *L. bishopi* is found in Saw Palmettos in South Florida. *L. geometricus,* The Brown Widow Spider, although very common amongst human habitations and debris, seldom bites, and is considered almost harmless. Fewer than a dozen of the Brown Recluse, *Loxosceles reclusa,* have been found in Florida. Thus today it cannot be considered a hazard. However, *Chiracanthium,* another seriously venomous small spider is definitely present. We have learned of many serious spider bite cases which we attribute to *Chiracanthium.*

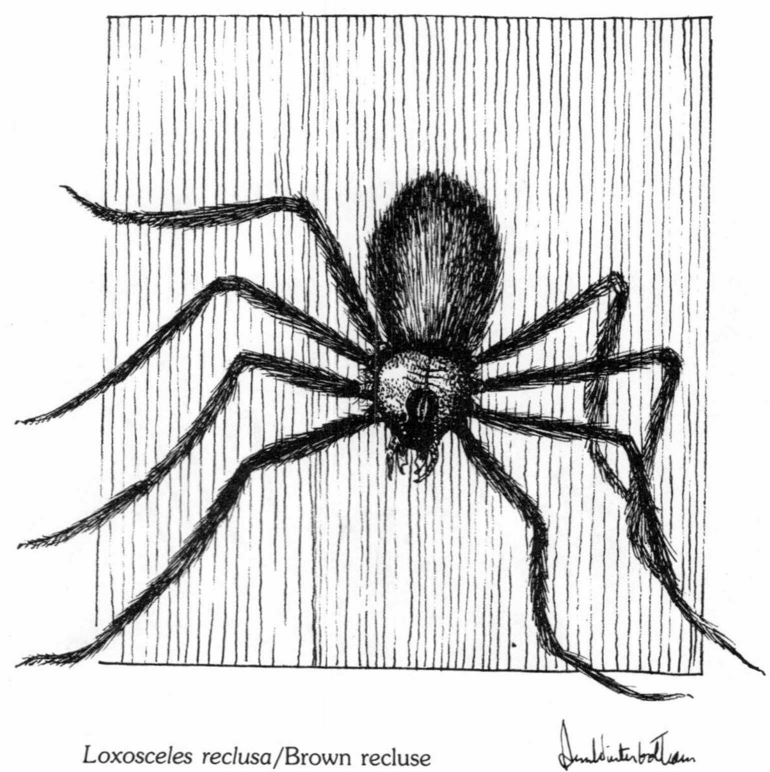

Loxosceles reclusa/Brown recluse

If you are bitten by a spider, preserve the specimen in alcohol—gin, vodka or whiskey will do if you don't have rubbing alcohol. Seek emergency medical aid, for both *Latrodectus* and *Chiracanthium* envenomation can be serious.

Note to paramedics and/or physicians: an antivenin for use in *Latrodectus* envenomation, produced by Merck, Sharp and Dohme, is available. Prepared from horse serum, it should not be administered without standard tests to check for horse serum sensitivity to reduce chances of anaphylaxis.

Chiracanthium mildei

CHIGGERS—RED BUGS

Chiggers are microscopic six-legged arachnids whose bite and concomitant salivary secretions cause intense itching. The much larger eight-legged adults are harmless. Standing or walking in wild places usually produces ample examples of chigger larva infestations, usually around the ankles. In cases where one sits or lies in grassy places, the infestations can be more troublesome.

They are sometimes called Red Bug—*Bête-Rouge.*

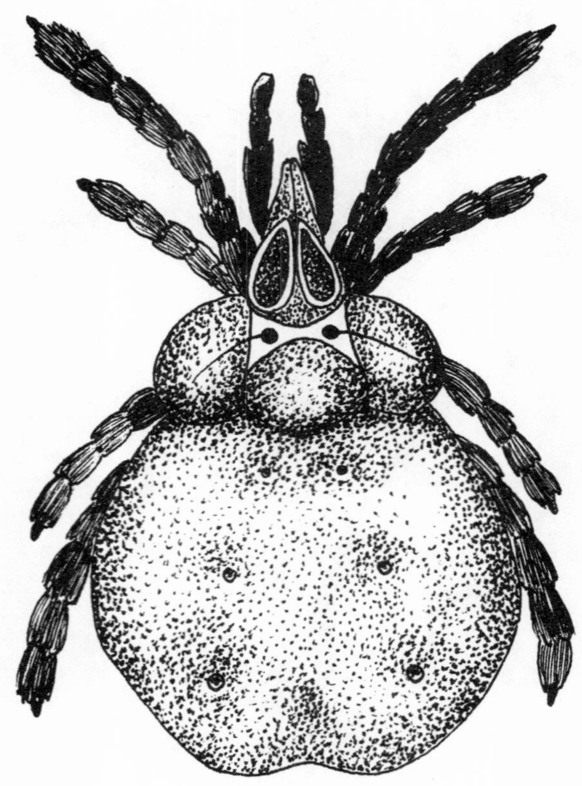

This is what a non-biting adult chigger looks like. In life it is about the size of a grain of rice.

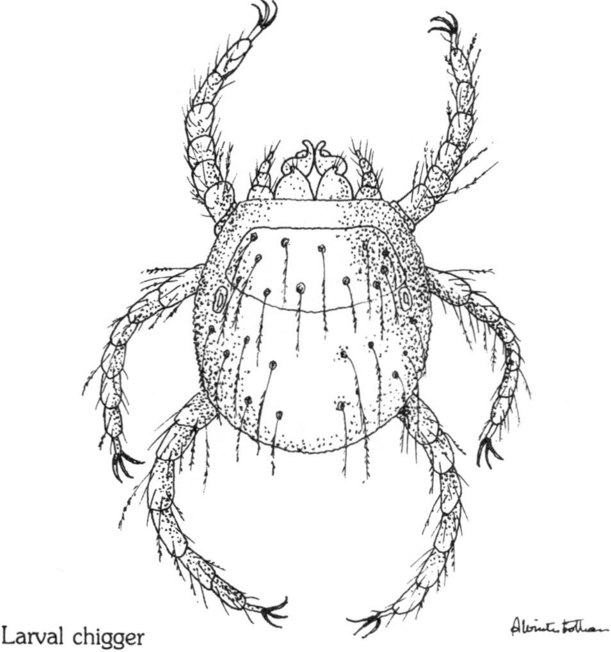

Larval chigger

Larval chiggers are minute, six-legged biters. Here shown is a chigger larva (schematic), which in life is smaller than a period.

FIRST AID

Apply vaseline or mineral oil which fills the animals' respiratory apertures, killing them by preventing their breathing. Some people recommend the use of nail polish as being lethal to the embedded creature.

SCORPIONS

There are several species of scorpions found in Florida, the most important being members of the genus *Centruroides*. Most adults are between one and three inches in length.

The scorpion's venom is delivered by the sting at the end of the long five- or six-segmented upward-curving terminal parts of the abdomen. Venom is neurotoxic and also contains cardiac toxins and agglutinins.

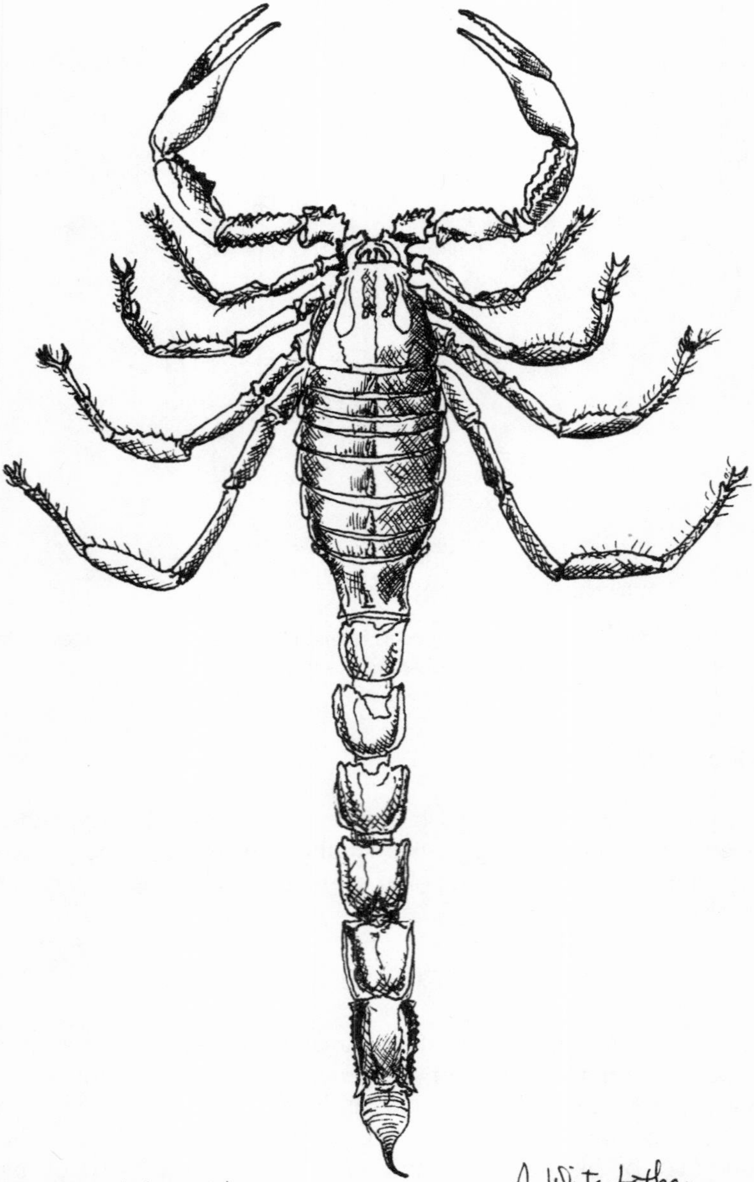

A scorpion (schematic)

A. Winterbotham

Florida species are not considered to be lethal in most cases. However one *could* be particularly allergic to scorpion venom, so if reaction to a sting is markedly painful or if nausea, vomiting or convulsions are present, then one should seek emergency medical aid.

In addition to *Centruroides* sp. pictured here, we have also shown the Vinegaroon, *Mastigoproctus giganteus,* a harmless Whip Scor-

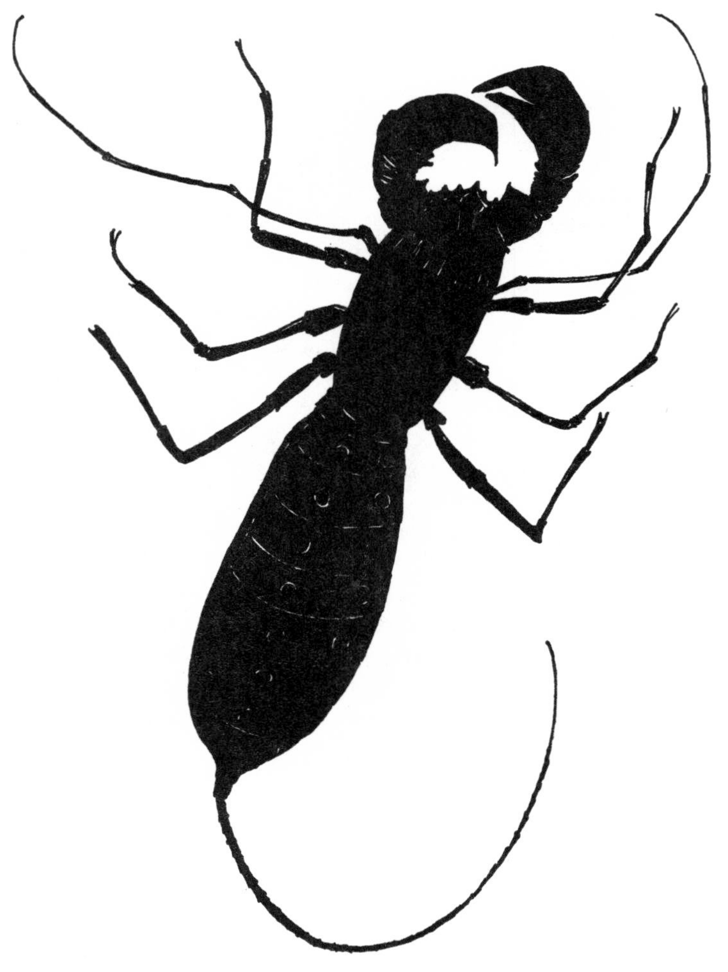

A harmless Whip-Scorpion

A. Winterbotham

pion. Although likened to an E.T. due to its horrifying aspect, it is *absolutely harmless* and should be encouraged in your garden because of its value in consuming noxious insects.

TICKS

Ticks are sometimes plentiful—usually in the cooler months. It is possible to pick up 20 or 30 on a short nature walk. Long-sleeved shirts and long trousers are helpful preventatives—especially if they are light-colored. One friend carried a vial of alcohol in which she dropped aggressive ticks (a much-deserved fate). After a winter's collecting, the vial of ticks was presented to an appreciative northern university museum.

Here pictured is a schematic Dog Tick, *Dermacentor* sp. Ticks do not vector disease here, to my knowledge, but they do cause poisoning—tick paralysis—mostly in dogs, but possibly also in children. Your dog might have twenty ticks happily making a living, mouth parts embedded in his skin, without appreciable harm. Number 21 might be picked up—a venom-equipped tick that attaches, usually in head or neck region—and intoxicates the animal, causing paralysis. The dog, if moving free, is likely to weaken and die of eventual starvation isolated in the woods. If you have him at home, search out and remove *all* ticks (then you will remove the offending one too), and in about 48 hours your dog will be as good as new.

As mentioned, tick paralysis is known in children too, but I know of no records in Florida. However, plenty of dogs have succumbed to this problem.

In removing ticks from yourself or your dog, use care not to break off and leave mouth parts to fester in the wound. Get it all out; application of oil or alcohol may help. Or ask your doctor to do it if the parasite attached to you is in an inconvenient-to-reach location—an unpleasant, embarrassing, and not uncommon circumstance.

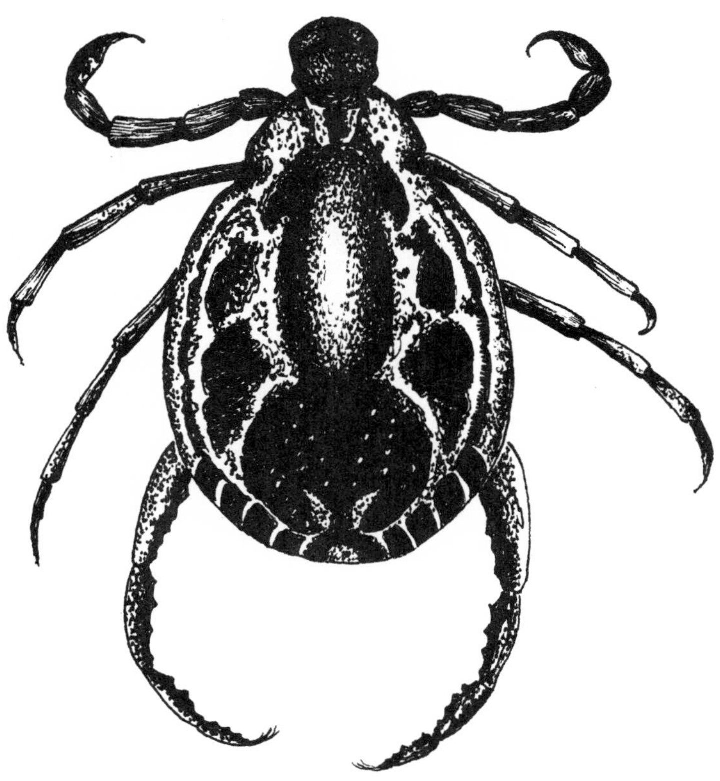

Dog Tick
Dermacentor sp. (schematic)

VERTEBRATE ANIMALS

CLASS REPTILIA
ORDER SQUAMATA

Suborder Serpentes, SNAKES
Suborder Lacertilia, LIZARDS

POISONOUS SNAKES

Florida is abundantly endowed with many species of snakes, only a few of which are really dangerously venomous. Outstanding among them are the Coral Snake, *Micrurus fulvius fulvius,* the Eastern Diamondback Rattlesnake, *Crotalus adamanteus,* and the Cottonmouth Water Moccasin, *Agkistrodon piscivorus.* Three others of lesser importance are the Dusky Pygmy Rattlesnake, *Sistrurus miliarius barbouri,* the Canebrake Rattlesnake, *Crotalus horridus,* which is confined to extreme north Florida and the Panhandle, and the Southern Copperhead, *Agkistrodon contortrix contortrix,* also common in a small area of the Panhandle. All other snakes in Florida are generally considered non-venomous.

The above listed forms are the only dangerous serpents native to Florida, but there are a lot of people moving animals around from where they are native to where somebody wants to put them. Florida is a major center for the wild animal trade. Thousands of dangerously venomous exotic serpents, everything from Boomslangs and King Cobras to Gaboon Vipers and dozens of other forms, are brought to Florida, mostly through Miami and Tampa, almost on a daily basis. It is not at all unusual for such exotic animals to escape and be found in many situations where they can be dangerous.

Two widely differing taxonomic groups are represented. The rattlesnakes, cottonmouths and copperheads are pit vipers, while the Coral Snake is closely related to the cobras of Asia and Africa.

Commonly, rattlesnake and other pit viper envenomation is immediately followed by edema and considerable pain. A good clean bite usually leaves two fang marks and by the time the patient reaches the doctor's office, enough time will have elapsed so that

Micrurus fulvius fulvius
Coral Snake
Any red, yellow and black banded snake with a BLACK snout in the S.E. United States is a Coral Snake

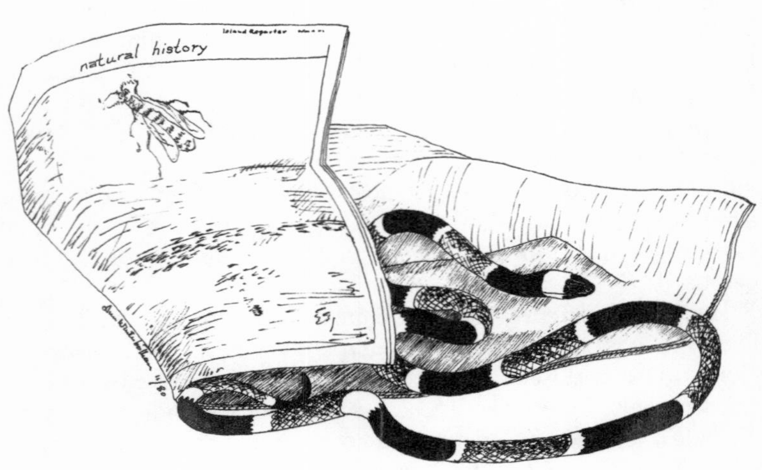

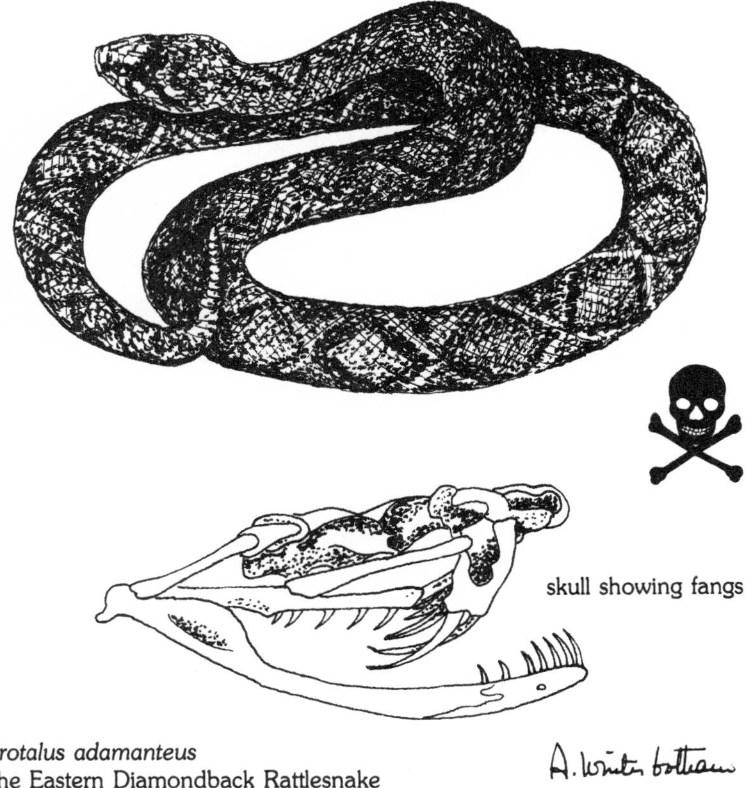

Crotalus adamanteus
The Eastern Diamondback Rattlesnake

with fang marks and edema and pain, a reasonable judgment of whether or not envenomation has taken place can be made. Ecchymosis (blood free of the vascular system lying under the skin) is present in almost every untreated Eastern Diamondback Rattlesnake envenomation* case. Although this snake is the largest and perhaps the most dangerous of all the world's rattlesnakes, bites are rare today because the species has suffered a substantial population decline with ever-increasing commercial development. However, it

*It is possible to be bitten by a venomous serpent without envenomation taking place. Sometimes the snake lacks a supply of venom. Sometimes, too, the bite is carelessly administered (from the snake's point of view) and little or no venom is injected.

is not impossible to find them on populated beaches because specimens sometimes wash down rivers from the interior of the state, often floating on debris. Sometimes rattlesnakes float far out to sea and later wash in on Gulf and Atlantic beaches. This occurred several years ago near Fort Myers when an Eastern Diamondback Rattlesnake crawled ashore among the reclining bikini-clad tourists. Hardly anyone noticed, and no one was hurt.

Another species that can cause a problem is the Coral Snake. It is much more common than the rattlesnake, but due to its retiring nature, burrowing habits and small size, it does not offer much of a threat.

Envenomation by a Coral Snake is not likely to occur for another reason: it is not very aggressive unless confined. The Coral Snake bite would probably have to be on the thin web of a finger or thumb or other tender part of the skin to be dangerous. It is highly improbable that a Coral Snake could bite a man's arm, for example. But a small child's arm might be envenomated.

A Coral Snake bite may be accompanied by no pain or perhaps only a little pain of short duration. Swelling may not occur, or may be slight. An abnormal sensation such as burning or prickling may be felt in the region of the bite and the victim may experience considerable weakness. Muscular incoordination may develop. Weakness, lethargy, salivation, difficulty in swallowing and visual disturbances follow. Breathing problems may result, with respiratory failure, accompanied by shock, heart failure and death. Coral Snake venom is primarily neurotoxic; rattlesnake, hemotoxic.

In the case of envenomation by any venomous species, first aid and early medical aid should be sought. Some Florida pharmacies stock both Coral Snake and pit viper antivenins. Neither of these sera should ever be administered without competent checking for serum sensitivity, else the patient might die of anaphylactic shock instead of snakebite. The actual names of the two antivenins are Coral Snake Specific Antivenin, prepared by Wyeth Laboratories, and Wyeth's Antivenin Crotalidae Polyvalent, which is used for our Eastern Diamondback Rattlesnake as well as for all other pit viper species found in Florida.

In the case of the rattlesnake, first aid includes a constriction band close to the bite, or above the first joint above the wound. This band should *not* be tight (not a tourniquet) but should be tight enough to stop the lymph flow and the superficial flow of venom. It should not impede the flow of blood in the arteries. Cutting and sucking is of value but only if done during the first hour after the bite.

For the Coral Snake, similar initial treatment is indicated, except that cutting and sucking is of little value.

Envenomation by an exotic species must also be considered here. It is well to realize that anything is possible with an escaped specimen, or an accident may occur with the exotic snake fancier himself. Fortunately, however, in most metropolitan centers, specific antivenom for almost any venomous serpent from any part of the world may be found. Such materials are available at Oklahoma City and St. Louis, for example, and the most complete collection of foreign antivenins I have ever seen is at the Detroit Zoo. In a matter of hours, any needed vial can be delivered anywhere in the country.

Poison control centers can be of help in most situations. The Oklahoma City Poison Control Center (Telephone [405] 271-5454), one of the very best in the country, stands ready twenty-four hours a day to help under even the most desperate and bizarre conditions. If you can supply the correct identification of the offending serpent, the people in Oklahoma can tell you within minutes where the nearest supply of the appropriate antivenin is located.

LIZARDS

There are only two venomous lizards in the world, the Gila Monster and the Mexican Beaded Lizard, both of genus *Heloderma*. Neither is found naturally in Florida but we do have lizards, skinks,

Eumeces inexpectatus
Southeastern Five-lined Skink

A. Winterbotham

that are thought by many to be poisonous (as distinguished from venomous). That is to say, they are thought by some to poison carnivores that eat them. Cats are thought by some veterinary researchers to sicken and become paralyzed after eating parts of the Southeastern Five-lined Skink, *Eumeces inexpectatus*, and other members of the same genus that occur in Florida. Some veterinarians disagree. Some call the condition "Lizard Poisoning," or Feline Vestibular Disease. The cat loses its sense of balance (ataxia) and can become paralyzed. This same phenomenon is observed in Africa when felines consume closely related skink species.

CLASS AMPHIBIA
AMPHIBIANS

ORDER ANURA
FROGS AND TOADS

In South Florida we have the exotic Cuban Treefrog, *Hyla septentrionalis* (also called *Osteopilus septentrionalis*). The skin is *warty*, unlike that of our native treefrogs. It may grow to five and one-half inches. The mucous secreted by the skin is toxic. In a cut, it will cause excruciating pain. In the eye, temporary blindness.

Bufo marinus, the South American Marine Toad, is prospering in many parts of South Florida. This species has a glandular exudate that is poisonous. It is best never to touch these very common animals.

Other amphibians of Florida are all harmless.

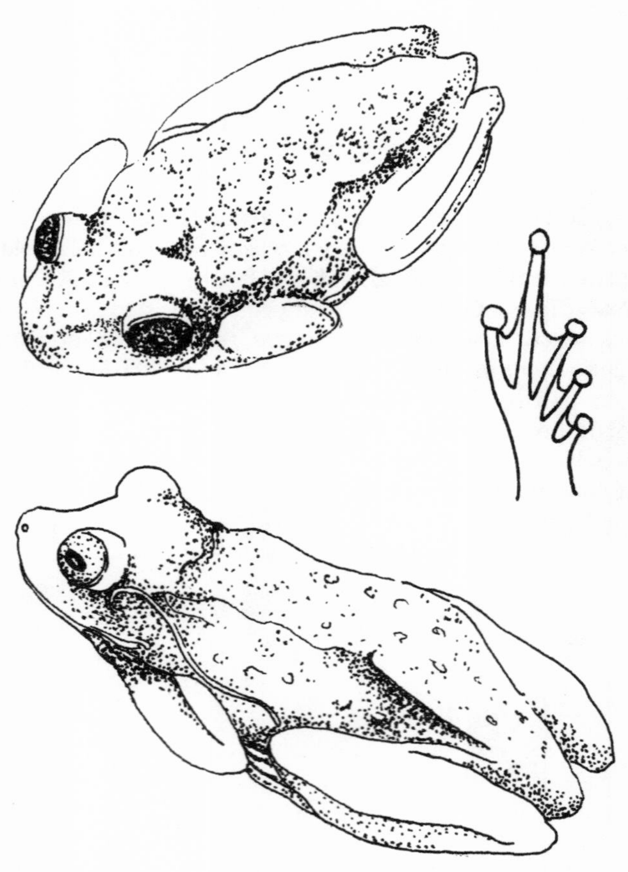

Osteopilus septentrionalis

CLASS CHONDRICHTHYES
CARTILAGE FISHES

STING RAYS

Flattened elasmobranch, cartilagenous fishes called rays are present, sometimes in great numbers, in the waters around Florida—usually in the warm months. Chosen to be pictured here is *Dasyatis say*, one of several Florida species. Toward the base of the tail are one or more barbed mucous-coated spines that, when driven into your foot or ankle, can cause excruciating pain. If driven through the abdominal wall, it can cause death.

Avoid Sting Ray stings by swimming in your pool. Or, if you must go into the sea, scuffle your feet. This helps prevent contact. Avoid snorkling in very shallow water. It is thus that the rare abdominal Sting Ray wounds have occurred—all fatal.

First Aid

Irrigate or soak wound in a very hot solution of Epsom Salts. If you don't have Epsom Salts, use very hot water. Heat supposedly alters the venom chemically. Seek emergency medical aid.

To the paramedic or physician: remove spines or fragments of spines, foreign contaminants in the wound, and the mucous or integumentary sheath, which comprises the toxic material. Suture as required. Administer Tetanus Toxoid booster if indicated.

There are several species of marine catfish in Florida waters, the pectoral and dorsal spines of which can inflict a painful puncture wound. Such wounds, although not nearly as serious as Sting Ray stings, should be treated as above.

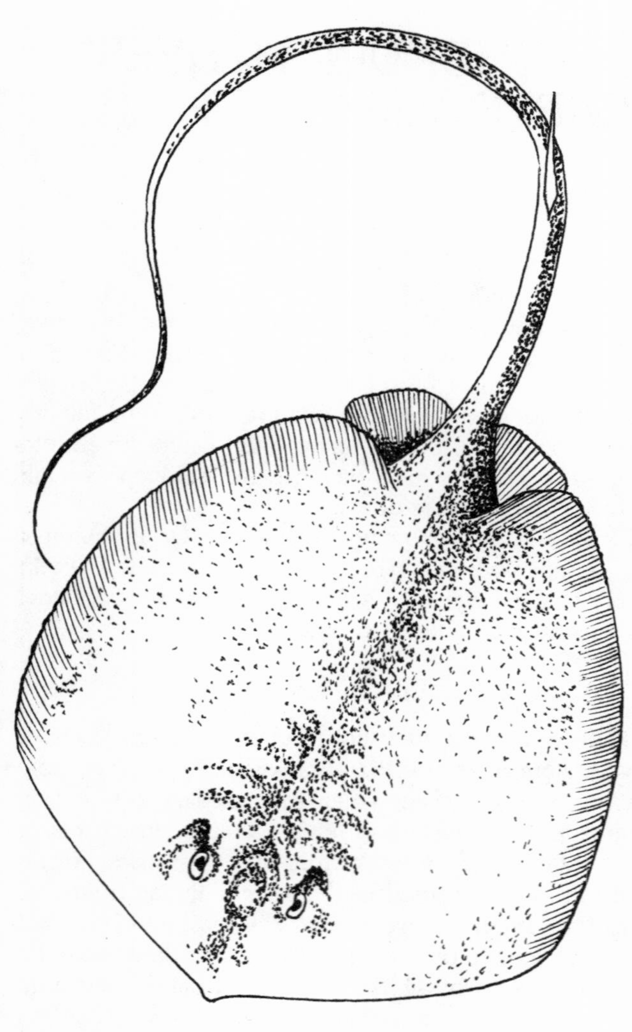

Dasyatis say

A. Winterbotham

CLASS PISCES
BONY FISHES

PUFFERFISH

FAMILIES CANTHIGASTERIDAE AND TETRODONTIDAE

Sphoeroides maculatus, the Atlantic Puffer, the form pictured here, is one of several Tetrodotoxic Fishes found in these waters. Although marketed as a commercial fish in the U.S., great care must be taken in dressing this and all puffers, else fatal poisoning can result. Tetrodotoxin is found in the liver, gonads, intestines and skin of Pufferfish and their close relatives. It is one of the most dangerous fish toxins known, causing incoordination, salivation, weakness, nausea, vomiting, diarrhea, abdominal pain, paralysis, convulsions and death.

In Japan, puffers of the genus *Fugu* are artfully prepared and consumed with delight. Each year some Japanese die of Fugu poisoning, a kind of Gastronomical Japanese Russian roulette.

When you hook a specimen of one of the several puffer species, enjoy it—watch it blow itself up into a balloon. Then release it, after which it floats like a beach ball for a moment, then burps out all of its flotation and swims rapidly away. Our advice is DON'T EAT PUFFERS! If you choose to ignore our advice, have the emergency medical phone number handy and available.

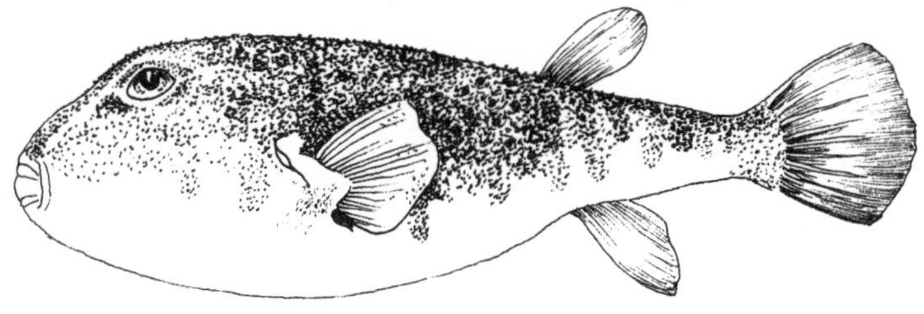

Sphoeroides maculatus

TOXIC FISH POISON

There are several kinds of toxic fish poison. Toxic fish poison is distinguished from toxic conditions due to bacterial decomposition of fish; i.e., spoiled fish, improperly iced. Toxic fish poisoning may be classified as:

Tetrodotoxic: already discussed (Pufferfish).
Ichthyocrinotoxic: glandular, not associated with venom apparatus. Found in morays, toadfish, cowfish, porcupine fish and puffers. Many other species in the world come under this heading, but the above are the ones likely to be known off Florida. The large Ocean Sun Fish that looks like a swimming fish head is pelagic in the Gulf, but rare. It, too, is ichthyocrinotoxic.
Ichthyohepatotoxic: as the name suggests, is contracted from eating fish liver, often of otherwise quite edible and delicious fish including some mackerel, some sea bass, and Porgy. Also, many shark species have been found sometimes to have toxic liver. Symptoms are nausea, headache, rash, fast heart beat, and peeling skin. Shark liver poisoning has resulted in coma and a few fatalities.

In each of the foregoing conditions the fish *contained* toxins dangerous for man* to eat. In the case of the following fish poisoning categories, the fish *occasionally* produce poisons dangerous to man when eaten. These fish poisonings are:

Ciguatoxic: The biological origin of ciguatera fish poisoning disease is not established for certain, but all indications point to a situation as illustrated in the accompanying food chain diagram. Tropical marine herbivorous reef fishes (parrot fishes, for instance) feed upon a plant containing the precursor of ciguatoxin. The herbivore is then eaten directly by man or a predator (a grouper, for instance, which has fed on the toxic herbivore is in turn eaten by man) who then may suffer from ciguatoxic fish poisoning. Plants most often suspected have been lowly blue-green algae which, after a storm, may be the first plants to recolonize a denuded area and offer the only available food to herbivores. Thus ciguatoxic fish poisoning is noted after hurricanes or other storms, and after man-created environmental deterioration resulting from dumping wastes (such as scrap metals on reefs) or alteration of an estuary, which

---

*Crocodiles too. In ignorance, the writer once fed a Pufferfish to a specimen of the endangered Indian Mugger Crocodile. The rare beast died within 12 hours.

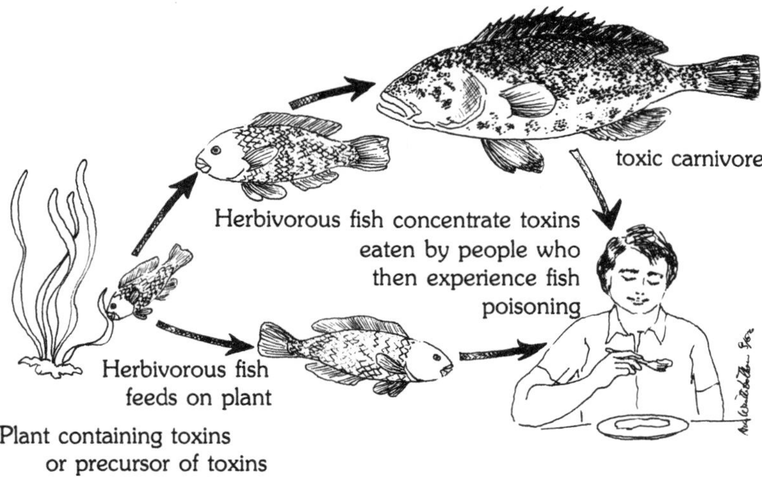

might affect the biology of reefs even far offshore. Older and larger predatory fish concentrate more toxin and are thus more dangerous than smaller fish of the same species. Barracuda, snappers, jacks and groupers are among the 300 species that have been implicated in ciguatera fish poisoning.

Symptoms appearing within the hour and developing for six to eight hours, include abdominal pain, vomiting, diarrhea, numbness of extremities and oral cavity, headache, vertigo, eyesight difficulties. Cold water feels hot, hot water feels cold. The toxin accumulates not only in fish, but in man. Thus subsequent eating of ciguateric fishes has a cumulative effect and the condition is exacerbated. There is about a 10% fatality rate in humans.

Ichthyoallyeinotoxic: Hallucinogenic fish poisoning. Mostly Oriental, but may appear in the New World. No fatalities recorded. Mullet and sergeant majors have been implicated. Most cases have resulted from eating fish heads, a common practice everywhere but the U.S.

Clupeotoxic Fish Poisoning: Here mentioned only for the purpose of completely listing the various categories of Fish Poisoning. Plankton-feeding fishes such as anchovies, some herrings and sardines are affected. Some students feel this is a kind of Red Tide phenomenon akin to paralytic shellfish poisoning (already discussed under protozoa) and due to the consumption of Dinoflagellates like *Gymnodinium.*

The various toxins implicated in fish poisonings are not, in general, destroyed by cooking or drying.

LIMITED GLOSSARY

alkaloids: complex, generally bitter compounds, most of which affect the heart and nervous system.

annual: a plant that completes its life cycle in one growing season.

anthelmintic: used to destroy intestinal worms.

axil: the upper angle between a leaf stalk or petiole and the stem that bears it.

berry: a type of fruit which is usually more or less fleshy throughout.

capsule: a closed, many-seeded fruit which when dry, splits along two or more lines and has more than one row of seeds.

caustic: capable of eating away or destroying with chemical action.

coma: a condition of insensibility.

convulsion: a violent uncontrolled series of muscular contractions.

CNS: central nervous system.

delirium: a state of frenzied excitement.

diarrhea: abnormal and frequent discharge of fluid stools from the intestines.

dilation of pupils: enlargement of the pupils in the eyes.

drupe: a fruit type, fleshy on the outside and with a stony pit enclosing a single seed.

edema: swelling.

emesis: vomiting.

emetic: an agent that causes vomiting, such as syrup of ipecac, a strong solution of table salt, a strong solution of prepared mustard, or strong soapy water.

epithelia: protective surface tissues.

GI: gastro-intestinal.

gills: platelike structures on the bottom of the cap, bearing spores, in a mushroom.

glabrous: not hairy.

glycosides: complex chemical compounds which when broken down under certain conditions yield a sugar plus another compound (aglycone) which may be poisonous. There are several types of glycosides such as:

cyanogenetic, which yields sapogenins that cause gastro-intestinal irritation;

cardiac, in which the aglycone is a heart stimulant.

ID: identification.

inflorescence: the arrangement or grouping of flowers in a branch system.

I.V.: intravenous.

lanceolate: narrow, with widest point near the base and tapering to a point at the apex.

leaflet: the bladelike portion of a compound (divided) leaf.

legume: the fruit or seed of leguminous plants; practically any dry fruit which splits along two lines and contains one row of seeds.

nausea: uneasiness of the stomach with a desire to vomit.

nystagmus: rapid and involuntary movement of the eyeball.

obovate: inversely ovate with the narrow end at the base.

opposite: two leaves at a node; two leaves opposing each other at any one place on a stem.

ovate: shaped like an egg, with the basal end broadest.

oxalates: salts or esters of oxalic acid which are toxic in high concentrations.

palmate: radiating from a common point; palmately-veined or palmately-divided leaf.

perennial: plants that live year after year.

perianth: collective term for the sepals and petals of a flower.

petal: one unit of the inner whorl of sterile leaf-like parts of a flower; usually colored and showy.

petiole: the stalk of a leaf.

phytotoxins (toxalbumins): highly toxic proteins similar to bacterial poisons.

pilose: velvety

pinnate: like a feather in being arranged along a central axis; pinnately-veined or pinnately-divided leaf.

pistil: the central structure(s) of a flower which develops into the fruit after fertilization.

poison: a substance that usually kills, injures or impairs an organism, through its chemical action.

pollen: minute granular structures produced in the anthers of a flower appearing usually as a fine dust and necessary for sexual reproduction in seed plants.

principle: a constituent of a substance, especially one giving to it some distinctive quality.

pubescent: covered with short, soft hairs.

raceme: an elongated and slender inflorescence in which the pedicels are attached to a simple central axis.

rachis: leaf stem of a compound leaf.

resins or resinoids: miscellaneous group of compounds which have a direct irritation on the nervous system or muscles. Some are extremely poisonous even in small quantities.

respiratory: pertaining to the lungs and other breathing organs.

rhizome: an underground stem, often horizontal.

salivation: an excessive discharge of saliva from the mouth.

seed: a ripened ovule after fertilization of the egg; embryonic plant within a protective coat, which will germinate into a new plant.

sepal: one unit of the outer whorl of sterile leaflike parts of a flower; often green, but sometimes colored.

simple: a leaf blade which is not divided into leaflets.

SLE: St. Louis Encephalitis.

sp. species.

spp. species, plural.

spasm: an uncontrolled and unnatural muscular contraction.

spore: a primitive minute structure, not a seed, which is capable of developing into a new individual; a reproductive body in non-seed plants.

stalk: stemlike structure at the base of a flower or leaf.

stamen: the part of the flower in which the pollen is produced; the pollen-bearing organ of a flower composed of anther (pollen sac) and filament (stalk).

titer: the strength of concentration of a substance in solution as determined by titration.

toxic: poisonous.

tremor: an involuntary trembling, shivering or shaking.

tuber: swollen and fleshy underground stem.

venin: toxic substance in venom.

venom: poisonous substance normally secreted by some animals; material that is poisonous.

whorled: three or more leaves at a node.

BIBLIOGRAPHY

Arnold, Robert E, M.D. *What to do About Bites and Stings of Venomous Animals.* New York: Macmillan, 1973.

Cooley, George R. "The Vegetation of Sanibel Island, Lee County, Florida." *Rhodora, Journal of the New England Botanical Club.* 1955.

Department of the Navy, Bureau of Medicine and Surgery. *Poisonous Snakes of the World.* Washington, D.C.: U.S. Government Printing Office, 1967.

Emboden, William. *Narcotic Plants.* New York: Macmillan, 1979.

Halstead, Bruce W., M. D. *Poisonous and Venomous Marine Animals of the World, Vols. 1–2.* Washington, D.C.: U.S. Government Printing Office, 1965.

Hardin, James W. and Jay M. Arena. *Human Poisoning from Native and Cultivated Plants.* Durham, N. C.: Duke University Press, 1974

Hecker, E. "Cocarcinogenesis and Tumor Promotors of the Diterpene Ester Type as Possible Carcinogenic Risk Factors." *J. Cancer Res. Clin. Oncol.* 99: 103–124. West Germany, 1981.

Kingsbury, John M. *Poisonous Plants of the United States and Canada.* New York: Prentice-Hall, 1967.

Langone. "The Quest for the Male Pill," *Discover,* October, 1982.

Lewis, Walter H. and Memory P. F. Elvin-Lewis. *Medical Botany.* New York: John Wiley and Sons, 1977.

Liener, Irvin (ed.) *Toxic Constituents of Plant Foodstuffs.* New York: Academic Press, 1969.

Long, Robert W. and Olga Lakela. *A Flora of Tropical Florida.* Coral Gables: University of Miami Press, 1971.

Morton, Julia F. *Plants Poisonous to People in Florida.* Miami: Hurricane House, 1971.

Smart, John. *A Handbook for the Identification of Insects of Medical Importance.* London: Jarrold and Sons, 1948.

Taylor, W. and Norma Farnsworth (eds.). *The Catharanthus Alkaloids.* New York: Dekker, 1975.

Trosko, James E. and Chia-Cheng Chang. "Environmental Carcinogenesis: An Integrative Model." *The Quarterly Review of Biology*. June, 1978.

Tyler, Varro, Lynn Brady and James Robbers. *Pharmacognosy*. Philadelphia: Lea and Febiger, 1981.

Voss, Gilbert L. *Seashore Life of Florida and the Caribbean*. Miami: E. A. Seemann Publishing, 1976.

INDEX

Boldface page numbers indicate illustrated species.

Abortifacient, 53
Abrin, 3, 67
Abrus precatorius, **66**–67
Aedes taeniorhynchus, 131–**132**
Agavaceae, 20–21
Agave, **20**–21
Agkistrodon
  A. contortrix contortrix, 147
  A. piscivorus, 147
Alkaloids, 3, 31, 35, 69, 85, 87, 89, 91
Allamanda
  Pink or Purple (*Cryptostegia grandiflora*) **44**–45
  Yellow (*Allamanda cathartica*), **28**–29
Allamanda cathartica, **28**–29
Alocasia, 41
"Aloe," American (*Agave*), **20**–21
Amanita
  A. muscaria, **12**–15
  A. virosa, 13
Amanitaceae, 3, 12–15
Amanitine, 13
Amaryllidaceae (Daffodil Family), 20–21
Amines, 3
Ammocallis rosea, **30**–33
Amphibia, 153–154
Anacardiaceae, 22–27
Angel's Trumpet (*Datura candida*), **84**–85
Annelida, 123
Anopheles, 131
Ants, 127
  Fire (*Solenopsis*), 127
Apocynaceae, 28–37
Araceae, 33–41
Arachnida, 135–143
Aralia (*Polyscias*), **42**–43
Araliaceae, 42–43
Aroeira (*Schinus terebinthifolius*), **22,** 23, **24,** 25
Arsenic, 67
Arthropoda, 125–143
Arum Family, 38–41
Asclepiadaceae, 44–45
Astrophyton, **118**–119
Atropine, 85, 87
Australian "Pine" (*Casuarina equisetifolia*) 11, **46**–47

Bahamas, 51
Balsam Pear (*Momordica charantia*), **52**–53
Basket Star (*Astrophyton*), **118**–119
Beefwood (*Casuarina equisetifolia*), **46**–47
Beefwood Family, 46–47
Bees, 127–129
  Honey, **128**
Bellyache Bush (*Jatropha gossypifolia*), 5, **62**–63
Bitter Gourd (*Momordica charantia*), **52**–53
Black Eyed Susan (*Abrus precatorius*), **66**–67
Bluefoot Psilocybe (*Psilocybe caerulipes*), **14**
Boat "Lily" (*Rhoea spathacea*), **48**–49
Box Thorn (*Lycium carolinianum*), **88**–89
Brazilian Pepper (*Schinus terebinthifolius*), **22,** 23, **24,** 25, 27, 127
Brevitoxin B, 107–108
Bright Eyes (*Catharanthus roseus*), **30,** 31, **32,** 33

Bristle Worms
Green (*Hermodice carunculata*), 123
Orange (*Eurythoe complanata*), 123
Red-tipped (*Chloeia viridis*), **122**–123
Brittle Stars, 119
Brughansia candida, **84**–85
Bufo marinus, 153
Burger, William, 67

Cajeput (*Melaleuca quinquenervia*), **74**–75
Calcium oxalate, 41
Cancer. See also Co-carcinogens.
Catharanthus roseus used in treatment of, 31
Candelabra "Cactus" (*Euphorbia lactea*), 6, **54**–55
Canthigasteridae, 157–158
Carcinogens. See also Co-carcinogens.
evidence of in cycads, 17
Cardol, 23
Caryota mitis, **76**–77
Caryota urens (*C. mitis*), **76**–77
Cashew, 27
Cashew Family, 22–27
Cassiopeia xamachana, **115**–116
Castor bean (*Ricinus communis*), 3, 63, **64**, 65
Castor oil, 65
Casuarina equisetifolia, **46**–47
Casuarinaceae, 47
Catharanthus roseus, **30**, 31, **32**, 33
Catfish, 155
Centruroides, 139, **140**, 141
Century Plant (*Agave*), **20**–21
Cerasee (*Momordica charantia*), **52**–53
Cestrum
C. diurnum, **80**–81
C. nocturnum, **82**–83
Chalice Vine (*Solandra guttata*), **90**–91
Charantin, 53
Cherokee Bean (*Erythrina herbacea*), **68**–69
Chiggers, **138–139**
Chiricanthium mildei, 135–**137**
Chloeia viridis, **122**–123
Chlorogenic acid, 81, 83
Cholera, 134
Choline, 13
Chondrichthyes, 155–156
Christmas Berry (*Lycium carolinianum*), **88**–89
Christmas Flower (*Euphorbia pulcherrima*), **58**–59
Chrysops, 134
Ciguatera fish poisoning, 158–159
Cineole, 75
Co-carcinogens, 5–7, 55, 57, 59, 61, 63
Coelenterata, 112–117
Commelinaceae, 48–51
Cone shells, **120**, 121
Alphabet (*Conus spurius*), 121
Crown (*C. regius*), 121
Florida (*C. floridanus*), 121
Conus, **120**, 121
C. atlanticus, 121
C. floridanus, 121
C. gloriamaris, 121
C. regius, 121
C. spurius, 121
Conmigo Ninguem Pode (*Dieffenbachia*), **38**–39
Contraceptive, 73
Coontie (*Zamia floridana*), 7, 11, **16**–19
Coral, 113–114, 116–117
Coral Bean, Eastern (*Erythrina herbacea*), **68**–69
Coral Plant or Tree (*Jatropha multifida*), 5, **62**–63
Coronarine, 35
Cortisone, 6–7
Crab's Eye Vine (*Abrus precatorius*), **66**–67
Crape Jasmine. See Jasmine.
Criminal's Delight (*Datura metel*), **86**–87
Crotalus
C. adamanteus, 147, **149**, 150
C. horridus, 147
Crown of Thorns (*Euphorbia milii*), 6, **56**–57
Cryptostegia grandiflora, **44**–45
Cucurbitaceae, 52–53
Culex nigripalpus, **130**–131
Curcin, 63
Cyanea capillata, 116

Cyanide, 3
Cycadaceae, 16–19
Cycads, 7, 16–19
Cycasin, 17

Daffodil Family, 21
Daphane, 5
Dasyatis say, 155, **156**
Datura, 3
  D. candida, **84**–85
  D. fastuosa (*D. metel*), **86**–87
  D. metel, **86**–87
  D. stramonium, 85
Daubentonia punicea, **70**–71
Dead Man's Skin (*Melaleuca quinquenervia*) **74**–75
Deathcap Mushroom (*Amanita phalloides*), 13
Dengue, 131
Dermacentor, 142, **143**
Destroying Angel (*Amanita virosa*), 13
Devil's Trumpet (*Datura metel*), **86**–87
Diadema antillarum, **118**–119
Dieffenbachia, **38**–39
Digitoxin, 37, 45
Dinoflagellates, 107–108
Diptera, 131–134
Do-Not-Touch-Me Sponge, (*Fibulia*), **110**–111
Downy Thorn Apple (*Datura metel*), **86**–87
Dragon-Bone Tree (*Euphorbia lactea*), 6, **54**–55
Dumb Cane (*Dieffenbachia*), **38**–39
Dysentery, 134

East Indian Rose Bay (*Ervatamia coronaria*), **34**–35
Echinodermata, 119
Edison, Thomas, 45
Eggplant (*Solanum melongena*), **94**–95
Elephant ears (*Xanthosoma*), 41
Elkhorn (*Euphorbia lactea*), 6, 55
Encephalitis, 130–131
Ervatamia, 3
  E. coronaria, **34**–35
Erysodine, 69
Erythrina arborea (*E. herbacea*), **68**–69
Erythrina herbacea, **68**–69
Eumeces inexpectatus, **151**–152
Euphorbia, 6
  E. lactea, 6, **54**–55
  E. millii (or *splendens*), 6, **56**–57
  E. pulcherrima, **58**–59
  E. tirucalli, 5–6, **60**–61
Euphorbiaceae, 5–7, 54–65
Eurythoe complanata, 123
Everglades, 75

Fabaceae, 66–71
Farmer's Lung, 11, 47
Feline Vestibular Disease, 152
Fibulia, **110**–111
Fire Coral (*Millepora*), 116, **117**
Fire Sponge (*Tedania*), **111**
Fishes, 155–159
  Bony, 157–159
  Cartilage, 155–156
Fishtail Palm (*Caryota mitis*), **76**–77
Flies, 131, 134
  Biting Stable (*Stomoxys calcitrans*), 134
  Deer (*Chrysops*), 134
  Horse (*Tabanus*), 134
  House (*Musca domestica*), 131–134
Florida Holly (*Schinus terebinthifolius*), **22**, 23, **24**, 25, 27, 127
Florida Arrowroot (*Zamia floridana*), **16**–17
Fly Agaric (*Amanita muscaria*), **12**–15
Fly Mushroom (*Amanita muscaria*), **12**–15
Frilled Fan (*Euphorbia lactea*), 6, 55
Frogs, 153–154
  Cuban Treefrog (*Hyla septentrionalis*), 153–**154**
Fungus. See Mushrooms.

Garget (*Phytolacca americana*), **78**–79
Gifford, John, 75
Gila Monster (*Heloderma*), 151
Ginseng Family, 42–43
Glycoalkaloid, 93, 95
Glycosides (Glucosides), 3, 37, 45
Goiterogenic, 3
Gomphospheria, 108–109

Gonyaulax, **108**
Gossypium barbadense (*G. hirsutum*), **72**–73
Gossypium hirsutum, **72**–73
Gossypol, 73
Gourd Family, 52–53
Gymnodinium brevis, 107, **108**, 109, 159

Hairy Thorn Apple (*Datura metel*), **86**–87
Halabis, Stephan, 47
Hecker, E., 5–7, 57, 59
Heloderma, 151
Hendry County, 24
Hermodice carunculata, 123
Hornets, 127–129
Horse-Tail Tree (*Casuarina equisetifolia*) **46**–47
Hunter's Robe (*Rhaphidophora aurea*), **40**–41
Hura crepitans, 5
Hydroids, 113
Hyla septentrionalis, 153–**154**
Hymenoptera, 127–130
Hyoscyamine, 85, 87
Hypophorine, 69

Ingenane, 5–6
Insecta, 127–134
Immortelle (*Erythrina herbacea*), **68**–69

Jasmine
  Day (*Cestrum diurnum*), **80**–81
  Crape (*Ervatamia coronaria*), **34**–35
  Night-blooming (*Cestrum nocturnum*), **82**–83
Jatropha
  J. curas, 5
  J. gossypifolia, 5, 63
  J. multifida, 5, **62**–63
Jatrophin, 63
Jellyfish, 112–117
  Giant (*Cyanea capillata*), 116
  Upside-Down (*Cassiopeia xamachana*), 115–116
Jequirity Bean (*Abrus precatorius*), **66**–67
Jessamine. See Jasmine.
Jimson Weed (*Datura stramonium*), 85

Kingsbury, John, 71, 165

Lactrodectus
  L. bishopi, 135–136
  L. geometricus, 135–136
  L. mactans, **135**–136
Lantana
  L. camara, **96**–97
  L. involucrata, **98**–99
  L. ovatifolia, 97
Lantana, Wild (*Lantana involucrata*), **98**–99
Lantanine, 97, 99
Leguminosae. See Fabaceae.
Leurocristine. See Vincristine.
Lizards, 151–152
  Mexican Beaded (*Heloderma*), 151
Lochnera rosea, **30**–33
Loxosceles reclusa, 135, **136**
Lycium carolinianum, **88**–89
Lycopersicon esculentum, **94**–95

Maguey (*Agave*), **20**–21
Malaria. 131
Mallow Family, 72–73
Malvaceae, 72–73
Manatee, 107
Mango, 27
Man-o-War (*Physalia*), **112**–113, 116–117
Mastigoproctus giganteus, **141**–142
Matrimony Vine (*Lycium carolinianum*), **88**–89
Melaleuca leucodendron (*M. quinquenervia*), **74**–75
Melaleuca quinquenvervia, **74**–75
Mescal, 21
Miami, 147
Micrurus fulvius fulvius, 147, **148**, 150–151
Milk Tree (*Euphorbia tirucalli*), 5–6, **60**–61
Milkweed Family, 44–45
Millepora, 116, **117**
Mollusca, 120–121
Mollusks, **120**–121
  Red Tide concentrated in, 108
  Using coelenterate nematocysts, 116
Momordica charantia, **52**–53
Momordicin, 53

Monkey Puzzle Tree (*Euphorbia tirucalli*) 5–6, **60**–61
Moses Plant (*Rhoea spathacea*), **48**–49
Mosquitoes, 130–132
Muscarine, 13
Mushrooms, 11, 12–15
Muskol, 131
Myrataceae, 74–75
Myrtle Family, 74–75

Nematocyst, 113, **114**
Neriin, 37
Nerium oleander, **36**–37
Nero's Crown (*Ervatamia coronaria*), **34**–35
Nightshade Family, 80–93
Nightshade (*Solanum*), **92**–93
Noctiluca, **108**
No-See-Um (*Culicoides*), 131, **133**
"Nutmeg" Tree (*Jatropha multifida*), 5, **62**–63

Octopus, 116
Old Maid (*Catharanthus roseus*), **30**, 31, **32**, 33
Oleander Family, 28–37
Oleander (*Nerium oleander*), **36**–37
Oleandrin, 37
Organophosphates, 131
Osteopilus septentrionalis, 153–**154**
Oxalic acid, 21
Oxylates, 3
Oyster Plant (*Rhoea spathacea*), **48**–49

Palma-Christi (*Ricinus communis*), **64**–65
Palmae, 76–77
Palm Family, 76–77
Pea Family, 66–71
Pencil Tree (*Euphorbia tirucalli*), 5–6, **60**–61
Periwinkle (*Catharanthus roseus*), **30**, 31, **32**, 33
Phalloidine, 13
Phenothiazine, 87
Philodendron, *Rhaphidophora aurea* mistakenly called, 41
Phylloerythrin, 97, 99
Physalia, **112**–113, 116–117
Physic Nut (*Jatropha curas*), 5, 63
Phytolacca americana, **78**–79
Phytolacca decandra (*P. americana*) **78**–79
Phytolaccaceae, 78–79
Phytolaccine, 79
Phytolaccotoxin, 79
Phytotoxins, 3, 65, 162
Pisces, 157–159
Pistachio, 27
Poinciana, Dwarf or False (*Sesbania punicea*), **70**–71
Poinsettia
  P. cyathophora, 59
  P. heterophylla, 59
  P. pinetorum, 59
Poinsettia (*Euphorbia pulcherrima*), 5, **58**–59
Poison Berry (*Cestrum nocturnum*), **82**–83
Poison Ivy (*Rhus toxicodendron*), **26**–27
Poisonwood, 27
Pokeberry (*Phytolacca americana*), **78**–79
Pokeweed Family, 78–79
Pokeweed (*Phytolacca americana*), **78**–79
Polypeptides, 3, 13
Polyscias, **42**–43
Porifera, 110–111
Potato (*Solanum tuberosum*), **95**
Pothos (*Rhaphidophora aurea*), **40**–41
Precatory Bean or Pea (*Abrus precatorius*) 3, **66**–67
Protozoa, 107–109
Psilocybe caerulipes, **14**
Ptychodiscus brevis, 107
Pufferfish
  Atlantic (*Sphoeroides maculatus*), **157**–158
  Fugu, Japan, 157
Pulque, 21
Punk Tree (*Melaleuca quinquenervia*), **74**–75
Purple Queen (*Setcreasea purpurea*), **50**–51
Pyrethrum, 129

Radefeld, Denis, 5
Rattlebox (*Sesbania punicea*), **70**–71
Red Bugs, **138–139**
Red Tide, 107–109, 159
Reptilia, 147–154
Resins, 3, 23
Rhaphidophora aurea, **40**–41
Rhoea spathacea, **48**–49
Rhus toxicodendron, **26**–27
Ricin, 3, 65
Ricinus communis, **64**–65
Rosary Pea (*Abrus precatorius*), **66**–67
Rose Bay (*Nerium oleander*), **36**–37
Rubber Vine (*Cryptostegia grandiflora*), **44**–45

Sabal Palms, 26, 27
Sand Box Tree (*Hura crepitans*), 5
Sand Flies (*Culicoides*), 131, 133
  Furious Sand Fly (*Culicoides furens*), **133**
Sanibel, 22, 47, 81
Saponins, 3, 21, 23, 43, 71, 79
Saw Palmettoes, 135
Schinus terebinthifolius, **22**, 23, **24,** 25, 27, 127
Scoke (*Phytolacca americana*), **78**–79
Scopolamine, 85, 87
Scorpions, 139, **140**, 141
Sea Anemones, 113
Sea Cucumbers, 116, 119
Sea Slugs, 116
Sea Stars, 118–119
Sea Urchin, Black or Needle Spined (*Diadema antillarum*), **118**, 119
Sesbane (*Sesbania punicea*), **70**–71
Sesbania punicea, **70**–71
Setcreasea purpurea, **50**–51
She Oak (*Casuarina equisetifolia*), **46**–47
Shrub Verbena (*Lantana camara*), **96**–97
Sisal (*Agave*), **20**–21
Sistrurus miliarus barbouri, 147
Skink, Southeastern Five-lined (*Eumeces inexpectatus*), **151**–152
Snakes, 147–151
  Canebrake Rattlesnake (*Crotalus horridus*), 147
  Coral Snake (*Micrurus fulvius fulvius*), 147, **148,** 150–151
  Cottonmouth Water Moccasin (*Agkistrodon piscivorus*), 147
  Dusky Pygmy Rattlesnake (*Sistrurus miliarus barbouri*), 147
  Eastern Diamondback Rattlesnake (*Crotalus adamanteus*), 147, **149,** 150
  Southern Copperhead (*Agkistrodon contortrix contortrix*), 147
Solanaceae, 80–95
Solandra guttata, **90**–91
Solandrine, 91
Solanine, 91, 93, 95
Solanum, 3, 92–95
  S. americanum, **92**–93
  S. melongena esculentum, **94**
  S. tuberosum, **95**
Solenopsis, 127
Sphoeroides maculatus, **157**, 158
Spiders, 135–137
  Black Widow (*Latrodectus mactans*), **135**–136
  Brown Recluse (*Loxosceles reclusa*), 135–**136**
  Brown Widow (*Lactrodectus geometricus*), 135–136
  Chiricanthium (*Chiricanthium mildei*), 135–**137**
  Red Widow (*Latrodectus bishopi*), 135–136
Spiderwort Family, 48–51
Sponges, 110–111
Spurge Family, 5–7, 54–65
Sterility, 39
Sting Rays, 155–156
  Dasyatis say, 155–**156**
Stoller, James K., 5, 59
Stomoxys calcitrans, 134
Symptoms. See Index of Symptoms, page *173*.

Tabanidae, 134
Tampa, 147
Tannins, 23
Tedania, **111**
Tequila, 21
Terpineol, 75
Tetrodontidae, 157–158

Ticks
Dog Tick (*Dermacentor*), 142–**143**
Tigliane, 5
Toads
South American Marine Toad (*Bufo marinus*), 153
Tomato (*Lycopersicon esculentum*), **94**–95
Toxalbumins. See Phytotoxins.
Toxicodendron radicans, **26**–27
Trumpet Flower (*Solandra guttata*), **90**–91
Tunicates, 107
Typhoid, 134

Urushiol, 27

Verbenaceae, 96–99
Verbena Family, 96–99
Vinca rosea, **30**, 31, **32**, 33
Vincristine, 31, 33
Vinegaroon (*Mastigoproctus giganteus*), **141**–142

Wasps, 127–129
Weather Plant (*Abrus precatorius*), **66**–67
Whiting, M., 17
Whip Scorpion (*Mastigoproctus giganteus*), **141**–142
Wild Balsam Apple (*Momordica charantia*), **52**–53
Wild Cotton (*Gossypium hirsutum*), **72**–73
Wild Cucumber (*Momordica charantia*), **52**–53
World Health Organization, 6
Worms, segmented, 123

Xanthosoma, 41

Yellow Jackets, 127–**129**
Yucca, 4

Zamia floridana, 7, **16**–19

INDEX OF SYMPTOMS

PLANTS

Abdominal pain or cramps, 13, 17, 37, 67, 79, 93
Anorexia, 93
Apathy, 93
Ataxia, 17, 85

Breathing, difficulty in, 13, 39, 41, 45, 47, 49, 71, 73, 79, 81, 83, 93, 97, 99

Chills, 47
Cough, 47
Coma, 13, 21, 97, 99
Convulsions, 13, 63, 65, 79, 89

Dermatitis. See also Rash. 21, 27, 29, 35, 41, 49, 51, 55, 57, 59, 61, 75, 77, 97, 99
Diarrhea, 17, 23, 37, 41, 45, 53, 57, 63, 65, 67, 71, 93, 97, 99
Drowsiness, 37, 79, 93

Eyes
impaired vision, 37, 63, 65, 79, 85
irritation, 45, 55, 59, 61, 77, 91
pupil contraction, 13
pupil enlargement, 37, 87, 91
swelling, 23, 55, 59, 61
temporary blindness, 55, 57, 61, 77
watering, 13

Fear, 81, 83
Fever, 47, 63, 65, 83, 85, 87

Gastroenteritis, 23, 45, 63, 81, 83, 89

Hair, loss of, 31
Hallucinations, 13, 85, 87, 91
Headache, 81, 83, 85
Heartbeat
  fast, 67, 71, 83
  slow, 13, 37

Ileus, 31

Jaundice, 97, 99

Kidney damage, 21, 31, 75, 81, 83, 97, 99

Liver damage, 21, 81, 83
Lung congestion, 17, 23

Mouth
  dry, 85, 87
  frothing, 73
  watering, 13, 39, 83, 93

Muscular incoordination, 85, 87, 91

Nausea. See also Vomiting. 81, 83, 85, 93

Paralysis, 17, 83, 93

Rash. See also Dermatitis. 23, 27, 29, 35, 43, 51

Speech, loss of, 39, 41
Swallowing, difficulty in, 39, 41, 43, 85, 87
Sweating, 13, 75

Tinnitis, 81, 83
Trembling, 93

Urine, dark colored, 21

Vertigo, 37, 67, 69, 81, 83
Vomiting. See also Nausea. 13, 17, 23, 37, 39, 53, 57, 63, 65, 67, 79, 81, 83, 85, 93, 97, 99

Weakness, 93, 97, 99

ANIMALS

Abdominal pain or cramps, 129, 157, 159

Breathing, difficulty in, 129, 150

Coma, 158
Convulsions, 141, 157

Diarrhea, 157, 159
Eyes
  irritation, 108
  temporary blindness, 153
  vision impairment, 150, 159

Fainting, 129

Headache, 158, 159

Heartbeat, fast, 158

Itching, 131, 138

Mouth, watering, 150, 157
Muscular incoordination, 150, 157

Nausea. See also Vomiting. 141, 157, 158
Numbness, 159

Paralysis, 157

Rash, 111, 158

Skin, peeling, 158
Stinging (pain), 110, 111, 116, 119, 123, 127–129, 136, 139, 150, 153, 155
Swallowing difficulty, 150
Swelling, 129, 136, 147

Throat irritation, 108

Vertigo, 159

Weakness, 150, 157
Wheezing, 129

By the same author:

The Nature of Things on Sanibel
Jaws, Too: The Story of Sanibel's Alligators and Other Crocodilians

About the Author:

After four decades as a naturalist, traveling and studying the plants and animals in many parts of the world, George Campbell has returned to Florida.

He has found a land much changed from where he grew up and where he was trained at the university in zoology and botany. He now makes his home on Sanibel Island, actively involved in preserving the natural beauty he loved as a youth.

He is chairman of the Southwest Florida Regional Alligator Association and is International Coordinator for the Fund for Animals, Inc.

About the Illustrator:

Ann L. Winterbotham moved to Sanibel Island in 1966 from Massachusetts, where she was born and educated and taught art for many years.

In Florida, she has been active in conservation. Through her efforts as an original member of the "Ding" Darling Memorial Committee, progenitor of the Sanibel-Captiva Conservation Foundation, and chairman of the Sanibel Planning Commission, much of Sanibel Island remains a nature preserve.